THE ALPHA PLAN

Louis Proto is the author of *The Feeling Good Book* (1989), *Coming Alive* (1987), *How to Beat Fatigue* (1987), *Take Charge of Your Life* (1988) and *Who's Pulling Your Strings?* (1989). A graduate of London University and a Westminster Pastoral Foundation trained psychotherapist, he brings to his work with individuals and groups his experience over the last twenty years of both eastern and western methods of facilitating awareness, personal growth and relaxation. Eclectic in approach, he draws on a variety of sources such as holistic therapies, zen, yoga and meditation (which he practised for three years in India), and in his books has made these techniques for well-being and relaxation available to a much wider public. His unique approach has attracted the interest of the national press, and he has regularly been interviewed on radio and answered listeners' questions.

LOUIS PROTO

THE ALPHA PLAN
FOR TOTAL RELAXATION

PENGUIN BOOKS

PENGUIN BOOKS

Published by the Penguin Group
27 Wrights Lane, London W 8 5 T Z, England
Viking Penguin Inc., 40 West 23rd Street, New York, New York 10010, U S A
Penguin Books Australia Ltd, Ringwood, Victoria, Australia
Penguin Books Canada Ltd, 2801 John Street, Markham, Ontario, Canada L 3 R 1 B 4
Penguin Books (N Z) Ltd, 182–190 Wairau Road, Auckland 10, New Zealand

Penguin Books Ltd, Registered Offices: Harmondsworth, Middlesex, England

First published 1989
1 3 5 7 9 10 8 6 4 2

Made and printed in Great Britain by
Cox and Wyman Ltd, Reading, Berks.
Filmset in Linotron Meridien by
Rowland Phototypesetting Ltd, Bury St Edmunds, Suffolk

To Johnny Ville and Bolette Larsen

CONTENTS

The author wishes to thank Geoffrey G. Blundell for kindly authorizing quotations and the reproduction of typical Alpha and Beta patterns from *The Meaning of EEG: A study in depth of brain wave-patterns and their significance*, published by the Publications Division of Audio Ltd, London.

HOW TO USE THIS BOOK

The Alpha Plan for Total Relaxation is described in the central section of the book (Part Two). Readers may like to turn to this section first, to familiarize themselves with the *5 stages of the Alpha Plan* and *how to use the Plan*, whenever they can count on half an hour or more of undisturbed privacy to enjoy the experience of total and blissful relaxation of mind and body (the Alpha state).

Part One of the book is in the nature of an *introduction to the Alpha Plan*. It underlines, in the light of recent medical research, the urgent need today for a simple but effective method of ensuring, whenever we feel the need for it, the total *psychophysical* relaxation (i.e. of body, mind and emotions) which, besides merely relaxing the body, alone goes deep enough to repair the 'wear and tear' of daily stress, is prophylactic against stress-related disease, 'recharges batteries', promotes well-being and enhances quality of life.

Part One then prepares the way for *understanding why the Alpha Plan works* by examining in turn both the traditional, meditational 'pathways to Alpha' and the scientifically proven effective modern relaxation techniques on which the Alpha Plan is based.

Finally, Part Three suggests *how to adapt the Alpha Plan to avoid getting stressed in the course of the day* when it is not possible (for example at work) to practise the full Alpha Plan as described in Part Two.

PART ONE

AN ALPHABET OF STRESS – AND RELAXATION

1

BETA-PLUS FOR EFFORT

People under Stress

Mike is a tour guide. He works for one of the biggest tour operators in London, which flies in holiday visitors from the USA by the planeload, gives them a free sightseeing tour of London and then sells them other tours to places they have heard about, like Oxford, Stratford-upon-Avon, Bath, Stonehenge, Canterbury. They are escorted on these day tours by guides like Mike, who are paid to be informative, pleasant and amusing and, above all, not to leave anyone behind.

He enjoys working with people on holiday and his groups enjoy him, the Englishness of his accent and his sense of humour, the patience with which he answers the questions which reveal only too often that the questioner hasn't been listening to a word he's been saying over the microphone. What he doesn't enjoy are the hassles that go with the job. Built into it is a constant race against time: steering groups of sometimes 50 or so people through a packed Westminster Abbey and trying to make the Changing of the Guard at Buckingham Palace before 11.30; rounding them up again to get them back to their hotel so they have time for lunch before the next tour goes out at 1.00. Crowds everywhere at St Paul's and the Tower; competing with the other guides to be heard over the general din; no coach at the pick-up point because the driver has been moved on by a traffic warden; hold-ups due to traffic jams or the ones who are always late back, either because they got lost or because they stayed too long in the souvenir shop. After a day of playing encyclopedia, timekeeper, diplomat and Mother Hen, Mike is, as his American 'punters' would put it, 'bushed'.

Alan is in his last term at university, reading history. The prospect of finals looming ever closer fills him with something approaching panic. He feels swamped by the sheer volume of revision still to be done in the little time that remains before the degree examination. He is not sleeping well and looks pale and drawn. After spending most of the day going over the bulky files of notes he has forgotten ever taking, struggling to commit the facts to memory, it takes him ages to unwind when he eventually calls it a day and retires to bed. As he lies in the darkness trying to get to sleep his thoughts keep returning to the 'stock' questions from past exam papers. 'How *religious* were the French Wars of Religion?' 'Charles the Martyr. Discuss.' Like some crazed academic his mind babbles on through the night, arguing with itself over the part played by William the Silent in the Revolt of the Netherlands, William of Orange in the 'Glorious Revolution' and the bourgeoisie in the French Revolution. In the wee small hours Peter the Great and Catherine the Great compete in a nightmarish squabble inside Alan's head for the title of 'the real founder of Modern Russia', while he lies there in misery wondering if they will ever let him get off to sleep.

Kate is a marriage guidance counsellor, housewife and mother of three children of school age – and finding it increasingly hard to keep it all together any more. So many demands on her attention and energy, so little coming back . . . She feels drained, depressed, irritable, expected to play Good Mother both with her clients and her family, always listening but never heard. After a day at the Centre, cooking the family's dinner and getting the children off to bed, not only is she not available to her husband, she is positively resentful when he dares to want to discuss his problems at work with her.

Margaret is retired, a widow, lonely and increasingly anxious about her health. Her arthritis is painful and seems to be getting worse. Her doctor has told her that she will feel better if she tries to relax, but this is easier said than done. She doesn't know how to. Instead she makes herself more tense by worrying about the future. What's going to happen to her if she becomes bedridden? Who will look after her?

Jim is a property developer and a successful one. He is also a workaholic who never knows when to stop. He is quite unable to delegate, not trusting anybody else to do the job as well as himself, whether his partner, architect, workmen, or tax consultant. He has been feeling unwell for some time and was warned by his doctor to take a holiday or at least to slow down. He couldn't. One night he had severe pains in his chest and was rushed to hospital. He survived this attack and is back home again convalescing. But he is not getting well as fast as he could. He is fretting about his business deals and insists on continually ringing his partner to find out what's happening and to give advice. His wife is terrified that he will have a relapse if he does not learn to relax.

But the others too are at risk with their health because of the stress they are undergoing. Mike has taken on too much work this season, to recoup on last year's bad one and get rid of his debts. If he does not ease up he could well become another statistic in the rising toll of victims of a heart attack, the biggest killer in the western world today. Alan is becoming increasingly drained, not only by the intense studying he has to do, but also by lack of sleep and anxiety about passing his exams. He is a candidate not only for the B A Honours in History but also for what used to be called a 'nervous breakdown'. Kate, the professional counsellor, could do with some counselling herself before she gets seriously depressed. She knows how to nourish other people but not how to nourish herself and recharge her batteries. She has lost any joy she had in her work, her children and her marriage. Unable to ask for support and for what she needs (like many of us), she may well unconsciously make herself ill to get the experience of being given to, loved, looked after for a change. This could also be true of Margaret. With the quality of her life at zero, with nothing to do all day but brood over her pain, isolation and gloomy future, she is creating more and more a negative reality for herself that could eventually manifest itself in her body in a way more serious than her arthritis. As for Jim, his next coronary may well be his last.

The role played by stress in contributing to the onset of serious illness has been increasingly well documented since Hans Selye published his trail-blazing work *The Stress of Life* in 1956. The Professor of Experimental Medicine at Montreal's McGill University described how the heart muscle of rats put under stress in the laboratory underwent the same acute disintegration that had been found in autopsies on human beings who had died from heart attacks after exposure to stress. As Selye pointed out, stress is not always bad. Stressors can be stimulating, a spur to achievement, and sometimes actually speed up a cure when someone is ill. But if they are too acute and go on too long, they can kill.

Research by Lawrence LeShan, a New York doctor, suggested in the 1950s a correlation between bereavement (i.e. severe stress) and subsequent development of cancer. That LeShan's paper was accepted in 1959 for publication by the *Journal of the National Cancer Institute* was a sign that the medical profession was beginning to take seriously the importance of stress in contributing to ill-health. Two years earlier the consulting surgeon at Guy's Hospital in London, Sir Heneage Ogilvie, had startled his colleagues by suggesting that 'The happy man never gets cancer.' He had noted how often the onset of cancer followed on some disaster, like bereavement, break-up of a relationship or financial crisis, and suspected that the decisive factor was the person's inability to handle the stress generated. One wonders whether, instead of 'happy', Ogilvie should have said 'relaxed'.

What is a stressor? It is that which puts the body under stress rather than the actual stress (wear and tear that results in the body) itself. Stressors are legion, and our response to them varies widely. What might be exciting or challenging for you might be stressful for me, for example, moving house, catching a plane, or going for an interview. One method of measuring stress was devised in the 1960s by Dr Thomas Holmes and Dr

Richard Rahe at the University of Washington School of Medicine. They drew up a Social Readjustment Rating Scale, based on the case histories of 5,000 patients, listing 43 life events that seemed to precede major illnesses and rating them on a scale of 1 to 100. Supporting LeShan's hypothesis, high up on the list came loss and bereavement in any form, including death of spouse (100), divorce (73), and marital separation (65). The stress value of marriage was 50, being fired 47, retirement 45, pregnancy 40, troubles with the boss 23. How stressful taking on a mortgage is seems to depend on how much you borrow. Interestingly enough, even apparently benign life events can be stressful, including 'marital reconciliation with mate' (45), going on vacation (13), and even Christmas (12). (You may be relieved to know that getting a parking ticket is the lowest on the scale.)

Stressors that we take for granted abound in our cities and we, like harassed Mike, are exposed to them every day: crowds, noise, pace, sensory over-stimulation. In 1962 research among a small, quiet Italian community in Roseto, Pennsylvania, revealed a lower incidence of heart disease than among the inhabitants of neighbouring towns, less than half their death rate from this cause. Some of the inhabitants had left to seek work in neighbouring cities. When they were traced, the researchers found that these urbanized Rosetans now had mortality rates closer to the general average. Competing in the big-city rat race is a dangerous game, as Jim's wife (but alas not Jim) has come to realize. Jim is the type most likely to fall victim to what the World Health Organization declared in 1969 to be 'the greatest epidemic mankind has faced' – one-third of whose victims in both Britain and the United States are under the age of 65.

Other factors besides stress undoubtedly contribute to heart disease: diet, lack of exercise, obesity, smoking, blood cholesterol, family history. But Dr Ray Rosenman, a Californian cardiologist and member of one of the leading heart research teams in the USA, believes that the biggest single reason why the incidence of heart disease has increased so alarmingly is the sheer pace of modern living. He points out that in England a century ago Victorians ate the same as we do today and exercised less – but they did not suffer as much as we do from heart disease. This seems to be borne out by the investigation by the Harvard School of Nutrition into the health of nearly 600 Irishmen who emigrated to Boston. Their brothers remained in Ireland, a country where people eat more saturated fat (especially butter) than in almost any other country in the world. Those who went to America to find work in a big city enjoyed a healthier diet – yet eventually they developed more heart trouble than their brothers who had stayed at home in rural Ireland. Dr Rosenman and his colleague Meyer Friedman decided to check the blood-cholesterol levels of a group of accountants over a 6-month period, starting at the New Year. They discovered that the levels rose as the start of the financial year in April with its attendant pressures approached, and fell again after work-loads returned to normal. The accountants' diets and life-styles had not changed during this 6-month period, only the stress to which they were exposed.

Concurrently with this study of accountants, Friedman and Rosenman investigated the question of which type of person was more likely to get a heart attack. They classified as Type A 80 San Franciscan men in business and the professions who were considered by people who knew them well to exhibit 'a habitual sense of time urgency and excessive competitive drive'. They established a control group of men who did not show this sense of urgency or competitive drive and called them Type B. Type A was found to have had seven times more coronary heart disease than Type B, even though diets and life-styles were similar. Following this up, Friedman and Rosenman divided 3,500 healthy volunteers aged between 31 and 59 from Californian businesses, banks and airlines into types A and B. Nearly ten years later they found that 250 of these volunteers had had heart attacks. Of these, 70 per cent were Type As. None of the Type Bs had died.

Other research has produced evidence of greater blockage of the coronary arteries among Type A individuals than among Type B individuals. Not only do these researches suggest that people who can't relax and take their time are more prone to get a coronary than those who can, but they also suggest that their inability to do so is probably the biggest single factor in causing heart disease. Type As get more heart attacks than Type Bs even if their blood pressure is normal, their family history is healthy, and they don't smoke. The cholesterol level in the blood is as significant a contributing factor as the stress. But, as we have seen, stress can raise the cholesterol level. The message very clearly to us all, then (and especially if we are Type As), is SLOW DOWN, TAKE IT EASY, RELAX.

Are YOU Type A?

Most people are a mixture of Type A and Type B. Rosenman and Friedman recognize four divisions in each group, from high risk (Type A1) to low risk (Type B4). Test yourself with some of the questions below, based on what their interviewers are trained to look out for in the standard assessment interview.

DO YOU

~ bottle up your feelings?
~ speak emphatically?
~ often feel restless?
~ often frown, scowl, clench your teeth, clench your fist?
~ enjoy competition?
~ always play to win?
~ frequently get upset or angry?
~ get irritated when driving by being held up in traffic?
~ hate to be kept waiting, say in a bank line or in a restaurant?
~ prefer to do a job yourself instead of waiting for others to do it?
~ hate to leave jobs temporarily unfinished?
~ feel that time is passing too quickly?

~ try to get work done while eating alone or while in the toilet?
~ try to do jobs as quickly as you can?
~ like to walk fast?
~ look at your watch often during the day?
~ set yourself deadlines?
~ spend time on your hobbies only when you have nothing more important to do?
~ always turn up early for an appointment?
~ rarely stay long at the table after dinner?
~ find yourself thinking of other things while talking to someone?
~ finish other people's sentences?
~ try to make others get to the point quicker?

If you answered 'yes' to all or most of these it does not mean that you are doomed. But it does mean that you are in the rat race and feeling acutely the time urgency that plagues most of us in this Age of Speed in which we live. And that, like all of us, you really do need to learn to relax.

If we don't, as Kenneth Pelletier, director of the Psychosomatic Medicine Center in Berkeley has explained, a prolonged level of excessive stress produces alterations in neuro-physical functioning, creating the preconditions for the development of illness. Whether this illness in fact manifests itself, and if so in what form, depends on what we are prone to by reason of heredity, constitution or personality – and on whatever bug is going around at the time, for stress also weakens the immune system. Stressful feelings like fear, anger and depression have been shown to release a powerful immune-suppressant called cortisol that reduces the number of T-cells and interferon and increases T-suppressors. This has obvious relevance for anyone diagnosed as HIV positive, and it is not surprising that relaxation therapy in various forms is being included in 'body-positive' self-help programmes.

As well as contributing largely to what remain, despite the

publicity for A I D S, the biggest two plagues of the contemporary affluent western societies, heart disease and cancer, stress is linked with much other dis-ease. In 1958 research at McGill University revealed that of 40 sufferers from multiple sclerosis all but 5 had been under prolonged stress before their illness manifested itself, and relapse usually followed on the heels of renewed strain. It is not surprising that stress can affect the functioning of virtually every system in the body when we consider how many of them are activated in the 'fight or flight' response to it. We sweat, turn hot or cold, breathe faster or not at all, contract our stomachs, tense our muscles, speed up the heart's pumping . . . A short list of stress-related dis-ease would include also the following:

ulcers	tension headache
colitis	migraine
diarrhoea	asthma
diabetes	flu
arthritis	common cold
skin ailments	accidents
hypertension	alcoholism
backache	psychiatric disorders

It has been suggested that up to 75 per cent of all patients' visits to their doctor are to do with complaints related to stress. There are as yet no figures on how much absenteeism and how many industrial accidents are due to the same cause.

Herpes is a classic example of a latent viral infection that can remain dormant until made to flare up by exposure to stress. As long as 50 years ago it was found in experiments at the University of Vienna that cold sores could be made to erupt in patients under hypnosis by reminding them of painful experiences in their past. Encouragingly, the reverse has since also been shown to be possible, namely that cold sores can be removed by auto-suggestion. We shall be discussing this further in a later chapter.

Fortunately, too, the body gives us warnings that all is not well before disease establishes itself and symptoms of it appear. If we are aware enough to note and heed such warnings it is often possible to abort the onset of illness. As a medical student Selye noted how, in the early stages of illness, the syndrome of 'just being sick' made its appearance first: vague aches, upset stomachs, feeling unwell and so on. His teachers were not interested in these non-specific symptoms. But years later Selye was to suggest that they are significant as registering the body's first alarm signals. The price for ignoring them would depend on the strength of the body's immune system to handle the emergency – or, as he put it, its 'adaptation energy'. He likened this energy to oil deposits: once it is burned up, we are burnt out. This book is not only about how to replenish your vital energy and repair the daily 'wear and tear' on your body that we call stress. It is about the blessings that learning to relax deeply brings to *all* areas of your life.

2

THE MASTER KEY

Relaxation is essential if we are to avoid falling victim to stress-related disease. If we do fall ill, it will make all the difference to whether we recover or not if we are able really to rest and to allow the body to recuperate its vital force and repair the damage, and we shall be seeing how to use deep relaxation to help the healing process in a later chapter. In this chapter we look at the benefits that setting aside a short period every day for deep relaxation will bring.

Our lives, if they are to be worth living, must have *quality*. That means that they should not only be about survival but also be about enjoying, zest, emotional satisfaction, creativity and self-expression. Learning how to relax makes all these things easier. Indeed, it is the master key which opens many doors that otherwise remain firmly closed to us. Consider the following areas of living, for example, and how satisfaction and success very largely depend on our ability to relax. We will start with our appearance. Though this is obviously the most superficial, nevertheless it is very important for some people to know they look good, not only because it makes them feel good but because how they look helps them earn their living.

Looking Good

Regular practice of deep relaxation through, for example, yoga or meditation freshens you, makes you look younger. Looking good is less about cosmetics than about radiant good health. You are not likely to look radiant if you are drained, tense, worried or exhausted. It will show: in your pallor, the bags under your eyes, your dull hair, your tight jaw, your frown lines, your strained expression. You may have been blessed with the bone-structure of an Audrey Hepburn or a Capucine, or the good looks of a Timothy Dalton. But if you are emotionally uptight or grey with fatigue you could simply look either forbiddingly hard or just plain ill. Relaxation *softens*, and that goes for face muscles as well. Even the plainest person, when happy, enjoying, smiling, deeply relaxed, has a sort of beauty that comes from the softness of their expression.

Feeling Good

The biggest single reason for taking the trouble to learn how to relax completely is simply that it *feels* so good. In fact, when you relax deeply (in the way that will be described later) it feels not only good but positively blissful. 'Energy,' said William Blake, 'is delight.' The more energy you have the better you feel, more vital, more alive. What we mean when we say that 'Life feels good' is that we have enough energy to enjoy it. We have to get energy from somewhere. We get it from food, from the oxygen in the air, from sleep, from other people. But if we are habitually tense, geared for action even when there is nothing that needs doing, unable to let ourselves 'just be', we burn up a lot of this energy needlessly and then wonder why life seems so dull and boring. The answer is that our batteries are flat. How we experience life is always a reflection of our own energy levels, and our environment (or how we perceive it) is only as 'high' as we are. Whenever you are feeling 'down' the best way to bring yourself 'up' again is not to try to change anything 'out there', but to recharge your batteries by deep relaxation.

Enjoying Leisure Activities

Type A people are likely to get less pleasure in off-duty hours because of their tendency, almost a compulsion, to carry on working, if only in the mind. Their addiction to using the left side of the brain (the 'doing' side) turns even play into work. They have no time 'to stand and stare', for time is money to them. In order to be able to get blissfully *lost* in anything, whether in music, a spectacular sunset, your favourite hobby or a deliciously hot and fragrant bath, you have to be able to let the right side of the brain (the 'feeling' side) take over. Only via relaxation can this happen. To have fun, to laugh, to be playful, you have to be non-goal-orientated, to drop your uptightness and trust that it's O K to allow yourself to have a good time.

Rest and Sleep

Just because you may be curled up on a sofa does not necessarily mean you are recharging your batteries, any more than lying in bed with your eyes shut means that you are getting a good night's sleep. Relaxation will not happen automatically just because you happen to adopt a prone position. For blissful dozing off or enjoying simply just being, more is needed – a letting go of both the compulsive thinking in your head and the tension in your body. It is a sort of surrender, of the need to control or protect yourself, to keep going over your problems or plans and just allowing things to be the way they are for a while. In order to surrender in this way one needs to feel safe – and this is how one feels when one is relaxed. It is possible that much insomnia is due to a subconscious fear of losing control.

The Social Round

This, if one is not in the mood, can be a nightmare. After a particularly gruelling day at work, having to drag yourself out to a function arranged weeks before when you did not know that tonight all you would crave would be a quiet evening at home in front of the telly, a hot bath and an early night for a change . . . We have seen that how you experience what's going on around you will depend very largely on your levels of energy and uptightness. That includes the rivetingness or otherwise of the conversation over dinner, the ambiance in the restaurant, and the volume of background music. The latter, if you are feeling drained and fatigued, can be *deafening*. Have you ever been dragged on to a disco floor by an enthusiastic partner whose energy is as boundless as yours is plummeting? Don't. It's no fun, at least not for you.

Relating

Shy people get the worst of all worlds. Meeting new people is an ordeal and acquiring friends is heavy duty. Tense, gauche, they turn people off either by trying too hard to please or by appearing not to be trying at all. Not relaxed enough just to be themselves, either they try to be what they are not or put all they have into trying to make a good impression. Neither is a comfortable way of being with other people. And if you are not comfortable with me, neither will I be with you. Tension is catching. This is particularly true if you are living together. People who are close to each other become finely tuned to each other's vibrations, their moods. If you are tense I will feel it. And until I know what your tension is about it will be hard for me to feel relaxed. Is it me? Something I said? Similarly, it will be hard for me to be with you if I am feeling uptight, drained or preoccupied. My energy will be low and everything you say or do will tend to irritate me, above all if you make any sort of demand on me. One way or another, our relationship is impoverished by uncleared tension. There will be no humour in it, no fun. Even if we don't have a row over whose turn it is to wash up, we won't exactly be in a playful mood. And remember, the couple that plays together, stays together. Being able to relax with another person sweetens the relationship.

Sex

Being able to relax makes all the difference in the world to the enjoyment of sex. Indeed, if you are not feeling relaxed, if you have other things on your mind or you are very fatigued, either it won't be possible at all or you probably won't be in the mood for it. When you're hot, you're hot. When you're not, you're not. Your energy may need refuelling before you can work up steam.

Professionalism

Relaxed confidence in doing our job is rewarded in our culture. Without it many jobs and professions are automatically barred to us, especially those which involve facing, meeting or dealing with the public. Even if we have not fluffed the initial interviews or written examinations because we were a bundle of nerves, promotion may not be forthcoming if we prove unable to cope with the stresses of the job. Of course actors, television presenters, public speakers, salesmen and so forth (perhaps even policemen!) may get butterflies in the stomach before going 'on duty'. It is only human to feel nervous before a performance, and the more sensitive you are the more nervous you are likely to feel. And, as Selye observed, this sort of short-lived tension can be a spur to giving a more than mediocre performance. But if they can't get those butterflies under control they will soon be out of a job. We *expect* newscasters to be impersonal, models to be cool, after-dinner speakers to be witty, waiters to be affable, and our stewardess on the plane not to look as if she is expecting it to fall out of the sky at any moment. It is not 'nerves' that is the problem: the problem is not knowing how to control them, letting them stop you from relaxing into whatever it is you are doing, doing a good professional job.

Effective Performance

To become proficient in any art takes effort: study, discipline, dedication and practice. But once you have acquired the necessary technique, once it has become a part of you, you 'just do it'. It is the same whether it is the art of tying your shoelaces or a bow tie, or of performing in a theatre or on the concert platform. The mark of technical mastery is effortlessness. A master of any art makes it seem the simplest, most natural thing in the world. This is because he or she trusts their technique enough to relax into whatever it is they are performing, whether a role in a play or an opera or a violin or piano concerto. Good actors *become* the character they are playing. In a master class on film acting, Michael Caine stressed the importance of relating to the camera as if it were a friend. 'Film acting,' he told the young actors who had been trying too hard, 'is just relaxation. Any tension shows up in the close-ups.'

This is equally true of voice production. The professional speaker who forces his voice will soon lose it – and the only way to get it back again will be to give the vocal cords sufficient time to relax and recover. If singers strain, *bel canto* flies out the window. Unless they are sufficiently relaxed, the tenor will sound more hard than lyrical, the soprano will never make those difficult coloratura passages, let alone hit her top note fair and square. If the virtuoso pianist cannot master his nerves enough to give his total attention to the music, his will be at best a mediocre performance, at worst a disaster. He has to be free enough of tension for his fingers to respond exactly to his intention, and undistracted enough to be listening with total absorption to the sounds he is producing from his instrument.

One can concentrate without being tense. In fact one concentrates better when one isn't, because one is free to give full attention, to be totally available for what is required. This is true of performance in any activity, from performing surgery to counselling, from taking examinations to playing tennis, from chairing a meeting to judo. One wonders how much Winston Churchill's painting helped us win the war, or how great a violinist Yehudi Menuhin would have been without his yoga.

When we are tense our field of perception narrows and our co-ordination deteriorates. Accuracy goes, we move clumsily, tend to make more errors and are more accident-prone, whether while driving a car, chopping vegetables in the kitchen or participating in competitive sports. It was ability to relax on the big day that helped Torvill and Dean win their Olympic Gold. As Christopher Dean put it, 'It was like a hypnotic trance, in which all the work you have done before comes out of you.' Whether he knew it or not, he was in the state of Alpha, about which we shall be saying much more later.

Inspiration

Asked on a chat-show where she gets her material from, Bette Midler replied, 'Most of the stuff comes just before I fall asleep.' This experience of creative ideas coming to you when you are not trying, not forcing, not making an effort, is a common one. How often have you tried vainly to recall a name or a fact, given up – and it comes? Tension blocks communication between the conscious and the unconscious mind – which is the reason why it is easier to recall facts from the storehouse of memory when you relax.

Agatha Christie used to say that her best plots came to her while she was doing the washing-up. (One assumes that she wasn't resenting it and was therefore relaxed.) Some of the greatest insights and discoveries in the world have happened almost casually, in moments of relaxation after prolonged effort, like Isaac Newton in the apple orchard. It is as if the left side of the brain assembles all the relevant pieces of the jigsaw, but the right side of the brain sees the whole picture, sometimes in a flash of inspiration. And the right side of the brain comes into operation only when we stop making an effort and relax into *feeling*. When we are trying to reach an important decision we often get hopelessly confused by the sheer number of alternative possibilities. The more we rack our brains, the more of a headache it becomes. If we can leave it, take a break and forget our problem for a while, sleep on it, we come back to it refreshed, often finding the answer so obvious that we wonder why we didn't think of it before. Dreams are famous for providing answers, as Niels Bohr and Stravinsky, among others, found. If they had been too wound up to fall asleep that night the world might well have had to wait longer for both the model of the atom and *The Rite of Spring*.

Spiritual Insight

It may come as a surprise to some readers to see spirituality linked with relaxation. You may have been brought up in the tradition of 'muscular Christianity', with its emphasis on good works and 'fighting the good fight'. This is of course one aspect of this many-sided religion. But one of the main functions of religion is to bring us inner peace (i.e. freedom from psychological tension, for example fear), and Christianity is no exception. Not only does the theme of peace recur often in the Bible, but whenever it does, tremendous value is always associated with it. It is introduced right at the beginning of the New Testament, at Bethlehem. The first Christmas greeting ever sent included angelic peace and positive intentions (Luke 14), and for centuries thereafter *Pax vobis* ('Peace be unto you') was a standard response in the Roman liturgy. One of the titles given to the Messiah was 'the Prince of Peace' (Isaiah 6), and the idea of 'peace' is very central to the mission and teaching of Jesus. In the Sermon on the Mount it is to the peacemakers that Jesus gives the title 'children of God' (Matthew 5:3), while St Paul was later to tell his flock that it will be 'The peace of God, which passeth all understanding' that 'shall keep your hearts and minds through Christ Jesus' (Ephesians 4:14).

We know that Jesus himself loved to relax with warm-hearted people over dinner and wine and that he was criticized for doing so by the Pharisees, who confused being spiritual with being aloof and uptight. He castigated them for making other people uptight, just as he reproved Martha, 'cumbered about much serving', for not being able to relax like her sister Mary and to just be with Him (Luke 10:40). Martha had obviously missed the point of some of the most sublime words her Master ever uttered:

'Consider the lilies of the field, how they grow; they toil not, neither do they spin: And yet I say unto you, That even Solomon in all his glory was not arrayed like one of these.' (Matthew 6:34)

Time and time again in the New Testament we read of Jesus relieving people of their pain, their anxiety, their guilt, their fear. All these had been making them too tense to experience the 'Kingdom of God' within them. 'Come unto me, all ye that labour and are heavy laden, and I will give you *rest*' (Matthew 28). Not only are we to 'Take therefore no thought for the morrow' (i.e. stop worrying about the future), but we are to 'Become as little children'. If children do anything, they live very much for the present – and can trust, relax and play.

At times Jesus seems to be echoing the teachings of the Taoist sages Lao-Tsu and Chuang-Tsu, with their emphasis on a relaxed, flowing and spontaneous attitude to life. In non-Christian traditions the value accorded to deep relaxation for bringing us closer to the Source is paramount. What else are statues of the Buddha but those of a man who has totally relaxed into meditation and his own being and become 'a light unto himself'? In zen, the absence of tension is seen as one of the signs of enlightenment. In yoga, it is a pathway to it.

In all cultures the power of the deeply relaxed state to promote spiritual and bodily healing and insight has been recognized, from shamans to the Sufi dervishes, from the Delphic Oracle to Mesmer and Freud, right down to the meditators, mediums, and hypnotherapists of today. The ability to immerse oneself in this life-giving spring, the Alpha state, and to emerge refreshed and rejuvenated has never been either such an urgent need or so apparently hard to attain as in this turbulent and stress-ridden age of ours.

3

ALPHA FOR EFFORTLESSNESS

HOW DO YOU RELAX AFTER WORK?

DO YOU

- ~ pour yourself a drink?
- ~ switch on the television?
- ~ go jogging or running?
- ~ go swimming?
- ~ play tennis, squash, golf (not, of course, at the same time)?
- ~ go to a fitness, aerobics or martial arts class?
- ~ have a sauna and/or a massage?
- ~ soak in a hot bath?
- ~ spend time with your children?
- ~ potter around in the garden?
- ~ take the dog for a walk?
- ~ curl up with a good book?
- ~ get totally absorbed in something you enjoy doing (hobby, craft, DIY)?
- ~ go out to a restaurant or a pub?
- ~ play an instrument?
- ~ listen to music?
- ~ take a nap?
- ~ ring up friends and invite them over?
- ~ ring up a friend and just gossip?
- ~ have a night out on the town?
- ~ get stoned?
- ~ make love?
- ~ .... (any other)?

WHY DO YOU THINK THEY HELP YOU RELAX?

IS IT SOMETHING TO DO WITH

~   enjoying what you are doing?
~   freedom from pressure?
~   doing what *you* want to do?
~   having things done for you (e.g. meals served)?
~   exercising your body?
~   resting your body?
~   not having to concentrate?
~   getting actively interested in something?
~   feeling safe in familiar surroundings?
~   a change of scene?
~   peace and quiet?
~   being in a lively atmosphere?
~   being alone?
~   being in company?
~   . . . .   (any other)?

We all have our own favourite ways of relaxing, and we ring the changes on them depending on our needs at the time. For example, if we have been exposed to too many people for too long, we will probably opt for an evening alone with the television or a good book. On the other hand, after a whole day spent in studying for his history finals the last thing Alan feels like doing is reading or being on his own any more. He will find relaxation rather in coming back into the present and getting out and about, seeing his friends. Quite the reverse for Mike. After a day's guiding in town he's had more than enough of the big city and being available to everybody. He needs to find himself again in silent solitude, or perhaps in escapist entertainment. Both, however, would be refreshed by getting back into contact with nature and back into their bodies by taking some exercise, perhaps going for a long walk or a jog in the park.

Relaxing is a question of finding balance again after tension has pushed us too far in one direction. Whether the tension has arisen through stress, effort or boredom, and whichever way we try to get there, our experience of the relaxed state (if we are fortunate enough to achieve it) is more or less the same. Life becomes worth living, we feel ourselves again, we enjoy. The deeper our level of relaxation the more blissful it is. The higher our level of discomfort has been, the greater the degree of relief we experience when the source of tension is removed, rather like a stone in our shoe.

In Japan they have a child's toy called a Daruma doll. Made of wood, with a weighted base, the doll can be pushed any way you like but after a good deal of wobbling will always return to its original position. This is a good model of what relaxation is – a coming back to yourself after having been pushed around by the demands of your work and life-style, after being pulled off balance by the stresses and strains of modern living. A Tibetan lama has called it 'the natural state of the mind', i.e. a state of rest from which we move out and to which we return. This 'stasis' we call here the 'state of Alpha', because it is characterized by a particular type of electrical brain activity using mainly waves of a certain frequency called Alpha. The measurement of these waves is called electroencephalography (mercifully usually abbreviated to E E G), and is effected via contacts placed around the head.

When we are awake the usual rhythm of our brainwaves is predominantly on the Beta frequency. This is associated with thinking, doing, concentration, focusing on the outside world and problem-solving. Beta is our 'everyday mind'. While we are engaged in these activities the electrical activity of our brain is varying within the range of between 14 and 26 times per second (usually measured as cycles per second, indicated by the symbol Hz). Under stress we can go even higher, into fast Beta. When Mike is having a hard time with his tourists, when Alan is agonizing over his imminent examinations and Jim is fretting over losing business deals, they are on the Beta plus wavelength, perhaps up to 30 Hz. The greater the effort, the stress, the higher the frequency.

What happens when we relax? Our brainwaves slow down to the lower frequency of 8 to 13 Hz, which we call Alpha. The more we relax, the deeper we go into the Alpha state. If we slow down even more (below 7 Hz) we enter the Theta wavelength, the half-asleep or dreaming state. When we are in deep and dreamless sleep our brainwaves have slowed down to between ½ and 4 Hz. We are in Delta.

Just as Beta waves are associated with 'being on the go', the workday mind (and, also, that 'Monday morning feeling'), so Alpha waves are associated with that 'holiday feeling', feelings of wellbeing, of 'all being right with the world'. The deeper we go into Alpha, the more relaxed we feel. When we have gone down to the borders of Theta we are in the deepest relaxation possible this side of sleep. This is the type of Alpha that the Alpha Plan (to be described later) is designed to facilitate – a blissful, totally relaxed yet aware state. It is a deeply satisfying experience from which we emerge with batteries recharged.

The physiological changes accompanying the drop in brain wavelength frequency in the Alpha state indicate that a decrease in the rate of the body's metabolism is taking place when we relax. Like sleep, another hypometabolic state, being in Alpha causes our energy resources to be taxed less. In fact, apart from sleep (and hibernation), sinking into Alpha is the *only* way to achieve this deeply restful hypometabolism. There is a marked decrease in the body's oxygen consumption, more so than in sleep. Respiration slows down and the heart rate decreases by an average of 3 beats per minute. There is also a decrease in the level of blood lactate, associated with anxiety states. Finally, blood pressure also drops. What is happening is that the sympathetic nervous system is going into abeyance and the parasympathetic nervous system is taking over.

It should be obvious by now why the Alpha state is a very desirable state to be in as often as you can. Not only is it pleasant – even blissful – but it is the biggest single antidote to any form of stress, defined by Selye as 'the wear and tear on the body'.

The Alpha state is both restorative and reparative; it restores lost energy and *repairs* both body and mind, just as sleep does. Sometimes, however, to sleep is either not possible or not practical. When this is so, resting in Alpha will produce many of the benefits of sleep – and without taking up so much time! During meditation, for example, the rate of decrease in oxygen consumption averages between 10 and 20 per cent and occurs within a few minutes of starting to meditate. When we are asleep, on the other hand, our consumption of oxygen decreases only slowly. After 4 or 5 hours it is still only about 8 per cent lower than when we were awake and in Beta. Alpha waves are not commonly found during sleep. Alpha is in fact a curious state – like being as relaxed in your body as if you were asleep, yet being aware (more aware than when you are in Beta) at the same time.

Another way of understanding what happens when we relax is in terms of left side and right side brain. The left hemisphere of the brain is the one that is concerned with doing, thinking, logic, organizing. It is this hemisphere of the brain that has received most training in the course of our education. We spend more time in our schools learning to read, to write, to think logically, to define and analyse, to be articulate, than in right hemisphere activities like music, dancing, carpentry, playing. We are taught to work, to compete, to succeed – in short, to be tense – but not how to relax. The left hemisphere is the part of the brain we are using when we are concentrating, working, worrying, making an effort, trying to earn our living – i.e. when we are in Beta. When we are using our senses or our intuition, seeing things as a whole rather than in bits (analysing their individual components), we have moved over to the brain's right hemisphere and enter into the realm ruled by Alpha.

To switch thus from left brain to right brain (or, more accurately, to integrate left and right hemispheres) we have to slow down. It is not possible really to *feel* anything, to take anything in, if we are going too fast. We won't savour the fragrance of a rose, taste subtle flavours, really appreciate a piece of music, or be able to empathize with what others are feeling. Also, we have to allow ourselves to open up to experiencing, to feeling. When we are thinking we cannot feel: thinking antidotes, cancels out the possibility of feeling. We commonly confuse the two. Ask somebody how they *feel* about something and very often they will start their reply with 'I *think* . . .' Fritz Perls, the founder of Gestalt therapy, was fond of urging his clients to 'lose their mind and come to their senses'. In the Alpha state we open up and become more sensitive, more in tune with what is happening around and within us – which is why we feel more alive. The essence of deep relaxation, of the Alpha state, is being present-centred, in the body rather than in the mind, in the sensing rather than in the thinking function. It is integrating, refreshing, invigorating, satisfying – in short, a relief from tension of any kind, physical, mental or emotional. To be able to slip into it at least once a day for half an hour or so is the best prophylactic against stress disease there is, as well as bringing us that enhancement of quality of life in all areas which, as we have seen, goes with the ability to relax.

It is almost certainly true to say that everybody has been in the Alpha state at some time or another. It can happen when we have allowed ourselves to become so totally absorbed in enjoying something that all tension has temporarily dissolved. Some of us will be in Alpha, perhaps, while contemplating a spectacular sunset, listening to music, or feeling very close to someone. But the state of Alpha is an elusive one. Some days you will be doing your jogging, swimming, yoga, meditation or whatever is your favourite way to relax – and you are there. Other days, it just doesn't happen. You are not 'in the mood', 'can't get into it', have something on your mind. And you can't force it, any more than you can force yourself to go to sleep. One of the most unfortunate titles ever given to a book was *You Must Relax*. There can be no relaxation when there is pressure of any kind, any 'shoulds', any things that have to be done. Relaxation is a 'non-doing', a letting go. It happens by itself when you stop doing − and that includes thinking, which is either a rehearsal for future doing, or a recalling of past doing. The Alpha state, like sleep (the Theta/Delta states), comes of its own accord when the obstacles to it are removed.

What, then, are these obstacles to being able to enjoy sinking into the blissful state of Alpha at will? They are twofold: *tension* in the body muscles and any sort of *movement* in the mind. Since in fact body and mind are not separate entities but part of the same continuum, any tension or movement in either will affect our ability to relax. It will be obvious to everybody what is meant by 'tension in the body muscles'. What do we mean here by 'movement in the mind'? Really, if you observe, there is no such entity as 'mind'. There are only thoughts and feelings, ever changing, coming out of nowhere and disappearing into nowhere again. It is a never-ending process, or rather, procession − and it keeps us in Beta. These thoughts clamour for our attention and, depending on the charge they carry for us, give rise to feelings which in turn impel us to actions. We are incessantly pulled this way and that by our thoughts and feelings: it is a constant chatter inside our heads. We worry ourselves, scare ourselves, criticize ourselves, go over conversations we have had with others, re-run old 'movies' time and time again on the projector that is memory. Compulsive thinking gives us no rest. Not only that, but it burns up energy unnecessarily. Unless this activity is somehow suspended temporarily, or at least slowed down, there may be distraction but there can be no real relaxation. It has been proved that imagined threats are just as stressful to our bodies as real danger: the body does not distinguish between them and will go into the same 'fight or flight' response. If we can slow down our thought process, our muscles will not be receiving messages to prepare themselves for action, adrenalin will cease flowing, the body will be ready to go into 'neutral' rather than staying 'in gear'. To attain the Alpha state, we have to let go of the body's 'sympathetic' reaction to stress (named by W. B. Cannon the 'fight, flight or freeze response') and invite instead what Herbert Benson has called the 'relaxation response', mediated by the parasympathetic branch of the autonomic nervous system.

The chapters that follow are about how to sink into the Alpha state *at will*. There are pathways to total relaxation of mind, emotions and body that have been evolved both in eastern and western cultures and which have worked and continue to work for untold numbers of people all over the world. Some of these techniques, for example yoga, tai chi, meditation and zen, require rigorous discipline to master them. Others, like auto-genics and Transcendental Meditation, are easier to get the hang of, but still require one to sign up for training courses and cost money. One has to find a good teacher, go out to classes, perhaps after one has been out at work all day when it is the last thing one feels like doing. All these disciplines take up time, something that those of us who feel most urgently the need to learn to relax tend to lack. Few of these approaches are capable of being adapted to being used to enable us to handle the stress and tension of a busy day as these arise. One can hardly start practising tai chi or adopt a hatha yoga posture while sitting at one's desk in a busy office. Similarly, going into deep meditation while driving your car is not to be recommended.

The Alpha Plan for Total Relaxation is intended for those who want a sure-fire way to be able to relax deeply *whenever they want or need to,* or to get some respite from bodily tension, an overactive mind, or emotional turmoil *while it is happening,* whether at home or in the course of the working day. The Alpha Plan combines in a new, simple, yet effective formula five basic elements that recur over and over again in both traditional and modern approaches to relaxation. As we shall see in the next two chapters, each of these approaches emphasizes a particular element. The Alpha Plan is the first relaxation technique to combine all these elements in a unique and timely synthesis. It has been evolved to meet the needs of those of us today who have neither the time nor the inclination to seek training in relaxation disciplines, yet have got the message that we need to learn to relax if we are to improve both our health and the quality of our lives. A short cut to the restorative and blissful state of Alpha, it gets us there fast. Before we describe the short route, however, we should first explore paths to relaxation that take the longer way round.

4

THE EASTERN SEARCH FOR TRANQUILLITY

It is not surprising that so many people in search of deep psychophysical relaxation are practising techniques which originated in the East, for example meditation, yoga or tai chi. These and similar techniques were developed as part of training for enlightenment, which has been described as 'the ultimate relaxation experience'. Here in the West we do not have the concept of enlightenment. We would talk rather in terms of 'at-one-ment', or 'self-realization', or perhaps 'individuation'. One of the greatest contributions of the East to the world has been to chart with great insight and subtlety the pathways to the tranquillity and inner peace so sorely lacking in our own culture. Let us look at some of them in order better to understand on what principles the Alpha Plan for Total Relaxation is based.

Taoism

This ancient Chinese philosophy would be very familiar to the ecologists of our own day, and, indeed, to anybody who has ever consulted an astrologer or looks to daily horoscopes for guidance. For Taoism is very much about living in harmony with oneself and one's environment. For 2,500 years it has been one of the major underlying influences on Chinese thought. Whereas Confucius was more interested in day-to-day rules of conduct, his contemporary the Taoist sage Lao-Tsu was concerned with a more spiritual level of being, with how to live in tune with the ever-changing process we call Life. We find the same sentiments expressed in the Bible:

'To every thing there is a season and a time to every purpose under the heaven: A time to be born, and a time to die; a time to plant, and a time to pluck up that which is planted; A time to love and a time to hate; a time of war, and a time of peace.' (Ecclesiastes 3:1–8)

For Lao-Tsu this sense of timeliness was essential to cultivate to ensure harmonious living, to feel this sense of 'all being right with the world'.

According to legend, when he was very old Lao-Tsu rode off into the desert of North-West China to die. A gate-keeper who knew of his reputation for wisdom refused to let him pass through until he had written down his teachings for posterity. So in the 81 chapters of the *Tao Te Ching* we have the most well known of the four 'scriptures' of Taoism (the others are by Chuang-Tsu, Lieh-Tsu and Huai-nan Tsu). They are a guide to living one's life free from unnecessary tension and are thus very relevant to anyone interested in learning the art of relaxation.

For Taoism, 'non-doing' is the secret of effortlessness. Other ways of putting it would be 'going with the flow', 'acceptance', 'being adaptable', just as water adapts itself to the shape of a container. When you have no preconceived ideas or expectations as to how things should be going, anything that happens is good. As Chuang Tsu puts it: 'He who follows the Tao . . . does not clutter up his mind with worries, and simply adjusts himself to what is happening around him.' In the *Tao Te Ching* Lao-Tsu returns in chapter after chapter to this theme of 'letting things be'.

'The sage goes about doing nothing.' (2)
'If nothing is done, all will be well.' (3)
'Tao follows what is natural.' (26)
'Tao abides in non-action.' (37)
'Yielding is the way of the Tao.' (40)
'Stillness and Tranquillity set things in order in the Universe.' (45)

'The Sage works without doing.' (47)
'Practise non-action, work without doing.' (63)

'Non-action' here does not mean 'inactivity' but absence of tension and effort in whatever we happen to be doing. It is a distinguishing mark of the 'enlightened' man (i.e. the 'sage'), or what, in the West, Maslow has called the 'self-actualizing' man (or woman). My own recollections of meeting Krishnamurti (in his school at Brockwood Park in Hampshire) are not so much of what he said but of how he was – flowing, natural, totally *present*.

In view of the contemporary epidemic of stress disease, few would disagree with Lao-Tsu's charming understatement, 'It is not wise to rush about' (55), while his 'No fight, no blame' (8) could well be interpreted today as 'No fight or flight – no coronary'. The 64-dollar question for us is 'Are we *able* to do nothing?' Not surprisingly, living as we are in a culture that is geared to doing as much as possible in the least possible time, most of us are not.

'Who can wait quietly while the mud settles?
Who can remain still until the moment of action?' (15)

This 'waiting quietly' and 'remaining still' and allowing the 'mud' of tension and the 'urge to do' to settle is exactly what the Alpha Plan is about.

Buddhism

Whereas Lao-Tsu gives us only tantalizing glimpses of the possibility of a life without hassles if we stop being so busy, Buddha gives us more clues as to how to attain it. His whole system is geared to getting us off the treadmill (the 'wheel of suffering') of daily living in a world that bruises us at every turn. Lao-Tsu simply tells us that it is our resistance to the Tao, the flow of life, that is the problem, and just to relax and 'go with it'. Buddha asks us rather to look into *why* we make ourselves tense and to take responsibility for doing so, and therefore for the effects ('karma') that follow inevitably from the cause. Buddhism is *par excellence* the path of insight and awareness. It leads to that state of serene abiding-in-the-Self symbolized in *rupas*, statues of the Buddha. He called this state 'nirvana'. It is perhaps more meaningful to us to think of it as total psychophysical relaxation, the ultimate in Alpha. The statues are used in Buddhism not as idols but as reminders that this tranquil state is available to all of us if we are willing to learn how to attain it.

'Nirvana' means 'extinction'. What has to be extinguished to attain this tranquillity? The ceaseless desire of the mind to think, do, get and have which stops us from 'just being', experiencing who we really are from moment to moment. It keeps us on the treadmill, in the rat race. Day in, day out we toil on, the cheese of wealth, success, power, prestige dangled by the mind before us, greed for the 'more' planted like an electrode in our brains. Round and round we go, fretting, scheming, accumulating, repeating, ever on the way but never 'there', or, more accurately, here.

How to get off the wheel of compulsive thinking and doing? The traditional way of liberation from the tyranny of the mind is meditation, brought by Buddha to a fine art. In its pure form, meditation is simply a relaxing into oneself while remaining alert – and watching what happens. And what happens when one first starts meditating is that one realizes just how tense one is and what a chatter is going on inside one's head. In the East the mind is likened to a monkey: never still, restlessly jumping from place to place, clamouring for attention. Usually we are identified with it and are therefore unconscious of just how much we are controlled by it. It is only when we start to observe it (and therefore to disidentify with it) that we realize how disjointed, spasmodic – and, yes, crazy, it is. Sitting in meditation we watch the monkey-mind leaping, apparently at random, from branch to branch. 'Memories, dreams, reflections', worries, fantasies, snippets of conversation repeated . . . Thought-forms in words and images try to fascinate us like the

Sirens, enticing us to get lost in them. If, like Ulysses, we can resist their blandishments long enough, eventually they lose their power to distract us from anchoring ourselves in Alpha. The procession of thoughts slows down, thins out. The more one meditates, the more one starts to experience gaps in the thinking process, blessed moments of relief, inner stillness, peace. Not 'peace of mind', for if mind is there it is necessarily in movement, but what in zen is called 'no-mind'. Practising meditation in this way is to abort stress at source, for it is from thoughts that distressing feelings and exhausting or self-destructive activity are spawned.

Like all enlightened masters, Buddha devised techniques for his disciples to use to make their path to nirvana a less stony one. From his own experience he knew the tricks the mind will employ on the meditator to ensure that it continues to hold us in thrall. Some of these techniques are relevant to the Alpha Plan to be described later, so it will be appropriate to mention them here.

Passive Awareness

Sometimes called 'witnessing' or 'bare attention', passive awareness is a relaxing of concentration while yet remaining alert. It is to be just an observer, rather like watching a TV programme in which you are not the slightest bit interested simply because you have nothing better to do. The opposite of this would be *involvement*, for example, identifying with the star so much that what happens to him or her feels as if it is happening to you. When 'Jaws' is around you tense, when he surfaces you jump, when he gets his come-uppance you relax. You have allowed yourself to be caught up in a fantasy, the thought forms of a team of film-makers, and have chosen to be in the 'then and there' rather than in the 'here and now' – which is sitting watching a box with moving images on it. Our awareness is where our attention is – and that, experientially, is the same as saying that *we* are where our attention is. What we give our attention to is what we are choosing to experience. When we choose to get involved in a train of thought it is the same as if we have chosen to run a movie on a video – except that it is inside our heads. The more we get involved in this fantasy world the further we leave the real world behind. The reason we prefer to escape into fantasy (which is what thinking is) is usually to escape experiencing present reality. The mind is threatened when we simply stay with what is, for it always wants to be somewhere else.

The meditative exercise of passive awareness is an exercise in present-centredness and self-awareness. It is detached, impersonal, impartial, treating all things that it experiences, thoughts and sensations that arise, with equal indifference. To maintain this state you may have to go through a smoke-screen of boredom thrown up by the mind. If you can accept 'boredom' as just more grist to the mill of your awareness it eventually evaporates.

Watching the Breath

Giving attention to one's breathing while meditating is a useful device to help slow down the activity of the mind by giving it something to focus upon. Breathing too is very much a 'here and now' phenomenon, so becoming aware of it has the second advantage of making our awareness more present-centred. One does not attempt to alter the natural rhythm of the breathing. One simply gives passive attention to it, with or without counting the outgoing breaths. Maintaining this passive attitude is most important. Attempting to fight the mind is an admission of its reality, whereas by merely observing it we are trying to gain insight into its illusoriness, that it is merely a 'magic show'. Moreover, any attempt to suppress the thinking process will merely be one part of the mind fighting another, an effort that will keep us in Beta, whereas the descent into Alpha involves a letting go of effort. It is an allowing, not a doing.

Metta

The above techniques are 'meditation without seed' since they are contentless and consist of just witnessing (*vipassana*). 'Meditation with seed' is meditation on some core theme, aimed either at insight or at reversing the mind's natural proclivity for dwelling on negativity, for example, worrying or resenting others. We mention *metta* here as a forerunner of the visualization techniques for dispelling negativity which we shall be describing later in connection with the Alpha Plan.

Metta means 'loving kindness'. One starts this meditation by imagining that one is breathing in patience and kindness and breathing out all the tension and worry to which one has been hanging on. Having established this, one then visualizes the breath as light that spreads throughout the body and then out to other people. This light, this 'wishing well', is first extended to those we actually do love. From these one goes on to visualize as enveloped with warm light those for whom we feel some aversion or who we feel do not like us or wish us well. Finally, our compassion is directed out to all throughout the world who are suffering from whatever cause, be it pain, deprivation, injustice or delusion. It is important to include oneself in the list of recipients of these positive feelings, even more so if one catches oneself judging oneself for not really feeling as kindly as the technique requires.

Although *metta* may sound a little sanctimonious, psychologically it is a shrewd device for helping to get one into a more relaxed frame of mind. It is hard to relax if one is feeling hurt, anxious, resentful or hard done by. It is understandable that negativity breeds tension when we remember that the 'fight or flight' response is activated by just such feelings. Visualization, too, has been shown in our own times to be a powerful device for the integration and healing of both mind and body.

There is, of course, very much more to Buddhism than the above. But, remember, we are interested here in these traditional paths to enlightenment only for what they can tell us about the more ordinary and accessible state of Alpha. Buddha's last words, to his brother Anand, were: 'Be a Light unto yourself.' The Buddhist Way is something of a 180-degree turn, from looking outside ourselves for things to make us happy, to turning in (or tuning in) to our own centre, there to find peace and bliss. But the price we have to be prepared to pay for inner peace is to be willing to let go of the attachments that keep us hooked and face what we dread will be the emptiness and boredom of 'nothingness'. To quote old Lao-Tsu again: 'Empty yourself of everything. Let the mind rest at peace' (*Tao Te Ching* 16).

Zen

A merging of the two great streams of Taoism and Buddhism, zen integrated the *wu-wei* (non-doing) of Lao-Tsu with the 'mindfulness' (i.e. self-awareness) demanded by Buddha into a training aimed at achieving the ultimate experience of 'let-go' (*kensho*). Zen is full of paradoxes, combining an intensely disciplined approach to meditation with an insistence on spontaneity of response and effortlessness in action, of reverence for the zen master with an iconoclastic non-seriousness, of the ruthless ferocity of the samurai with the knockabout zaniness of the clown.

Zen practice is aimed at removing the filter of ideas, opinions, projections, memories and associations by which the mind interprets, dilutes and distorts our direct perception through the senses of everyday life and our experience of ourselves. Zen is against any form of intellectualizing and is intensely practical. It relies for enlightenment not on insight gained through reading scriptures, but on tackling – 'head-on' – the barriers the mind puts in our way to being natural, relaxed, flowing. The whole effort of a zen master is to jolt his disciple out of the left hemisphere of his brain into the right, out of *thinking* into *being* – and to ensure he stays there.

In the Rinzai school of zen a device called a *koan* is used to exhaust the capacity of the left side of the brain to the point where, temporarily, it gives up. A *koan* is, quite simply, a question impossible to answer, like 'What is the sound of one hand clapping?' But try to answer it the unfortunate disciple must, for after wrestling with this non-sense all day he is expected to come up with an answer to give to the zen master at the evening *darshan* (interview). And the zen master is never satisfied, whatever answer is given. Time after time the student is told he is wrong and that he must go back to his mat in the *zendo* (meditation hall) and try again.

For days, maybe weeks, he will wrestle with the *koan*, a slippery customer that constantly eludes his mind's attempts to catch hold of it. Pressure from the zen master steps up: he may pretend to be angry at the stupidity of the answer offered, fly into a rage and even clout the wretched disciple before throwing him out. Whatever else is happening, the disciple is learning that for once he gets no prizes for being merely clever – or rather, he is undergoing an 'unlearning' of relying exclusively on his intellect rather than his intuition – innate intelligence – to come up with the truth. He will in fact not be let off the hook until (for the time being) his mind is so totally fatigued that his response to the *koan* is non-intellectual, spontaneous, authentic and arising out of his awareness in the here and now. What specific form the disciple's response takes is (and always has been) unimportant. It may not even be a verbal one. Zen masters have been known to be delighted with apparently totally irrelevant (and sometimes irreverent) 'answers'. These could include the disciple picking up his sandals and putting them on his head, blowing a raspberry – or just getting up and walking out. What has pleased the master is how the disciple's response (whatever it is) shows that he is coming from a place undominated by logic and linear thinking, that he has been able to enjoy temporary freedom from his mind (*satori*) and now knows how that feels. But woe betide him if he tries to get through the next *koan* by repeating what worked this time. He will be lucky to escape with mere abuse or a thump on the head.

One zen story tells us how a master taught a young disciple not to copy him by chopping his finger off! Whether this actually happened or not is not important – except, of course, to the unfortunate disciple. The moral of the story is the essential message of zen: 'Be yourself – whatever that is – at all times.' But in order to be able to 'be yourself' you have to be free from tension in the mind. It is perhaps this sense of 'being yourself' that makes the Alpha state so deeply satisfying and why it has been called 'the natural state of the mind'.

Central to zen practice, especially in the Soto school, is the meditation of *zazen*, 'just sitting'. This is similar to the Buddhist 'witnessing' meditation (*vipassana*). Sitting cross-legged on a cushion, back straight, hands loosely joined with thumb and index fingertips lightly touching, with eyes half-open and unfocused, the meditator practises experiencing 'just sitting' totally, i.e. without distractions. Thoughts will come and go, but the meditator resists the temptation to follow any particular train of thought, just noting with indifference that they are there. This 'bare attention' is also given to external sounds and body sensations, maintaining a passive attitude. By and by the mind slows down, the body relaxes, Alpha (and, if meditation is going deep, Theta) brainwaves start to predominate over Beta . . .

> 'Sitting quietly,
> Doing nothing,
> Spring comes and
> The grass grows by itself.'

It helps, when the weeds of thoughts are noticed to be becoming rather too intrusive, to become aware of the lower part of the belly, called in Japanese *hara* or *tanden*. This serves the same purpose of helping to overcome distractions as watching the breath does in Buddhist meditations. Similarly, if one is getting drowsy, becoming more aware of the body posture and straightening the back helps in staying awake. (It is from observing a slumping back that the monk in charge of the *zendo* knows which of the meditators needs a whack on the shoulders with his big wooden spatula to sting him back into wakefulness.) When one considers that on *sesshins* (retreats) held at regular intervals in zen monasteries in Japan the meditators (many of them laymen joining the monks) may have been sitting for a week or more in two-hourly sessions, several times a day, they can be forgiven the odd straying off the path of relaxed awareness on their way to the state of 'no-mind'.

But the practice of zen is not limited only to wrestling with the mind in the *zendo*. The disciple will be expected to keep the same state of awareness while performing everyday chores like washing, cleaning, going to the toilet. Years ago, in the course of one *sesshin*, zen master Suzuki Roshi told a group of us: 'Everything is *zazen*.' This I took to mean that if one could learn to do one thing totally, 'just sitting', then one at least knew when one was not bringing the same total yet relaxed attention to anything else one might be engaged in doing. Once you have tasted the state of Alpha and recognized it for what it is, you realize when, at other times, you are in Beta – and the way out of it. Asked 'What is zen?' another master once replied: 'Zen is your everyday life.'

Yoga

It was in India, however, not in Japan, the home of zen, that the importance of body awareness for getting us out of the mind and into a deeply relaxed state was first recognized. The yoga postures now being practised by many in the West were developed by yogis over 2,000 years ago. In the second century BC they were set down in writing by Patanjali in the *Yoga Aphorisms*, together with the other teachings of yoga.

'Yoga' means 'union', and the postures of hatha yoga are designed to integrate body, mind, emotions and spirit for balanced and harmonious living. Patanjali warns us from the start that the biggest problem we have to confront if we want to experience this at-one-ment is our mind.

'This is the beginning of instruction in yoga.
Yoga is the control of thought waves in the mind
Then man abides in his real nature.
At other times man remains identified with the thought
    waves.'

This, of course, is reminiscent of the Buddhist insistence on 'mindfulness' and appropriately so, since Gautama Buddha was himself Indian and had tried out every contemporary approach to enlightenment (including yoga) before becoming 'a Light unto himself' – and working out his own 'Way' to guide other seekers.

Unlike many Western forms of exercise, yoga postures are static and aimed not at giving muscles a work-out but at stretching the spine, stimulating glands and calming the nervous system. One holds them without straining and feels the relaxing and energizing effect straight away. In 1961 in New Delhi Dr B. K. Anand reported the same increases of Alpha brainwave activity in yoga practitioners as were discovered five years later in zen meditators by Drs Kasamatsu and Hirai of Tokyo University. Beta is very much a 'head' phenomenon: it is associated with thinking, especially any form of negative thinking, and is stirred up by negative feelings which are a form of stress. If we wish to move out of Beta down to Alpha we have in some way to move energy down from the head into the body. Since energy follows in the wake of our attention (and our intention), we can do this simply by withdrawing attention from mind-games and becoming more aware of body sensations. To be centred in the body and to feel relaxed are the same thing.

Learning how to control and direct your own vital energy through the exercise of awareness is very much the training of all branches of yoga. Depletion of this energy (called *prana* by yogis), as well as intoxication of the bowel by unwise eating, is seen as the main cause of illness. The same concept is found in Taoist systems of healing (e.g. acupuncture), of energy (*chi*) which needs to be abundant, clear, balanced and flowing if we are to experience well-being. It is reminiscent too of Selye's 'adaptation energy', which, remember, he likened to a store of oil deposits, which, if used up, meant trouble.

Advanced yogis learn how to channel their energy up through the *chakras*, conceived of as different nerve centres in the body. One's experience of reality is considered to depend on which of the *chakras* one's consciousness is habitually centred in. The seven *chakras* and the preoccupations and values one would take for granted if functioning in each are (in ascending order):

1st *chakra* (base of the spine)	SURVIVAL
2nd *chakra* (pubis)	SEXUALITY
3rd *chakra* (solar plexus)	POWER
4th *chakra* (heart)	LOVE, FEELINGS
5th *chakra* (throat)	AUTHENTICITY
	CREATIVITY
	SELF-EXPRESSION
6th *chakra* ('third eye')	AWARENESS
	INSIGHT
7th *chakra* (crown of the head)	AT-ONE-MENT
	(ENLIGHTENMENT)

According to this model of the bodymind, the Beta states would appear to be linked with the more turbulent lower *chakras*, and Alpha states with the calmer reaches of *chakras* 4–7. This makes sense, for it is seeing the world in terms of a jungle, sexual rivalry or the rat race that makes for the stress and tension of 'fight or flight', whereas, as we have seen, cultivating 'loving kindness', 'being yourself' and 'mindfulness' make for the 'relaxation response'. Of the last *chakra* little can be said about the state of awareness that goes with living from it except by an enlightened master – a Jesus, a Buddha, a Gurdjieff, a Krishnamurti. It is the highest state of consciousness and attained by very few.

To still the mind to the point where one is sufficiently clear of distracting thoughts to relax into body awareness, yoga employs a number of useful devices. Relevant to the Alpha Plan is the device of focusing one's attention so that it is narrowed down to one point. What that point is is not important. But, for deep relaxation, maintaining 'one-pointedness' is, as is the sense-withdrawal that follows in its train naturally, antidoting any sensory overload we may have been subjected to and cutting out further input to the nervous system. The following are some of the ways this is done in yoga.

Gazing (Tratak)

This device consists simply of gazing at the flame of a lighted candle while sitting in meditation. One does not stare or strain the eyes – one simply observes with 'soft' eyes what the candle flame does, how it burns, now brightly, now dimming, unmoving, flickering . . . Normally, as C. Maxwell Cade has shown in experiments, Alpha waves disappear when the eyes are open, and it was formerly thought that the Alpha wave was linked to the visual process in the brain. We now know that whether you can stay in Alpha with eyes open depends on your attitude and that you can train yourself to do so. This is true of *zazen* and also of *tratak*. As one-pointedness starts to happen, so the brain activity of the meditator starts to spiral downwards from Beta to Alpha, his energy moves out of thinking into body awareness, and, from being scattered, into being centred in the here and now.

Repetition of Sounds (Mantras)

That sounds have the power either to disturb or to soothe is common experience. One of the stressors of modern city life that keep us in Beta is noise: of traffic, fire-engines, police sirens, pneumatic drills, the Saturday night party in the next flat, or the burglar alarm down the street that nobody seems bothered about . . . Until such racket is switched off it is hard for us to do likewise. And (the most important insight of eastern pathways to Alpha) that includes the inner racket created by our minds also.

To repeat silently a mantra to oneself has much the same calming effect as a lullaby has on a fractious child (hopefully). It does not much matter what word or words are chosen, so long as they are not intrinsically disturbing or have negative or emotive associations for us. (If they actually have calming associations, so much the better.) The mantra provides the focus for one-pointed awareness, while its repetition is of itself hypnotic.

Adapted by Maharishi Mahesh Yogi in the form of Transcendental Meditation, mantra yoga is probably the most widely practised form of meditation in the West today. That it effectively gets those who practise it regularly into Alpha has been demonstrated by experimental research conducted on TM meditators by Dr Herbert Benson, Associate Professor of Medicine at Harvard Medical School and Director of the Hypertension Section of Boston's Beth Israel Hospital. What Dr Benson termed the 'relaxation response', however, was found to be in no way unique to TM. There are many pathways to it, as we are seeing in this chapter and will do in the next.

Yogic Breathing

Attention to breathing is even more important in yogic practice than in Buddhist meditation. In yoga, breathing exercises are used not only to quieten the mind or to change moods, but also to charge the body with *prana*. There are many different breathing exercises, aimed variously at purification, revitalization, balancing yin and yang energies, and dispelling negativity. Sometimes they are accompanied by 'meditation with seed' (visualizations) or repetition of a mantra, which makes them even more effective devices for transforming energy and consciousness.

Other forms of yoga, not so well known in the West perhaps

as hatha and mantra yoga, seek to 'get you there' by other means, all geared to freeing one from tension, whatever its source. Jnana yoga resembles Buddhism with its intense inquiry into the basic question 'Who am I?', seeking (once again) to cut through identification with the mind. Closest to Christianity (and the Sufi branch of Islam) is bhakti yoga, the way of the devotee. The bhakti yogi is on the path of surrender to something greater than himself, in service to God or humanity. In this psychological surrendering of the ego's attachments and defences all tension melts, just as it does in the surrender of the sexual orgasm. Finally, there is the secret 'left-hand path' of tantra yoga, for initiates only, in which the bliss of at-one-ment is sought in ritualized sexual union (without orgasm). Startling (or even shocking) though this may seem to us, reared in a society that tends to polarize sex and religion, the earthly and the spiritual, it was not so in the culture which, along with yoga, produced the erotic sculptures still to be seen today in caves and temples in India and allowed Krishna not only his Radha but also his *gopis*.

5

WESTERN APPROACHES

As in the East, so in Medieval Europe it was in religious practice and the search for spiritual enlightenment that pathways to inner peace were charted. To these insights of the mystics have been added in the last century or so the experience of therapists, scientists and researchers. These have been more interested in the phenomenon of deep relaxation from the point of view of mental and physical well-being. With its scientific bias and technical know-how, the West has unravelled the 'how' of the Alpha state – what actually happens when we relax, and what happens when we don't. In the process many of the insights of Taoism, Buddhism, zen and yoga have been validated, both by quantum physics and by experimental research.

Christian Mysticism

Christian mystics speak of 'at-one-ment' rather than of enlightenment, of 'contemplation' rather than meditation, and of 'recollection' rather than of awareness or mindfulness. Yet they are talking about the same 'abiding in the Self' as the Taoists, Buddhists, yogis and zen masters. Alpha brainwaves are the same, whether our skin is yellow, brown, pink or black. If we know the pathways, the Alpha state is available to us wherever we may happen to be, in a *zendo*, in an *ashram*, in a monastic cell – or in our own bedroom at home.

Reading the medieval mystics, one finds them echoing the great meditational classics of the East (to which they could not at that time have had access). Meister Eckhart has the same aversion to conceptualizing as any zen master, especially about

God, 'who is of all names free, of all forms void'. This could be Lao-Tsu talking in the opening lines of the *Tao Te Ching*:

> 'The Tao that can be spoken of is not the Eternal Tao.
> The name that can be named is not the eternal Name.
> The Nameless is the beginning of heaven and earth.
> The named is the mother of ten thousand things.'

For Eckhart, the way to know this Reality is to seek to become one with it, not by thinking about it. It is the way of present-centredness, of emptiness ('spiritual poverty'), of detachment from the restlessness of the mind that prevents us from directly experiencing what is. The technique he suggests is that of cultivating a passive awareness.

'We ought to learn to keep an empty mind in all we do, but it is uncommon that an untrained person can manage this so that neither circumstances nor jobs bother him. Expert attention is necessary.' 'Doing', once again, gets in the way of 'just being'. 'People should not be concerned so much with what they do, but with what they are.' Eckhart confirms his preference for right-hand brain hemisphere functioning: 'The soul is troubled as long as it perceives created things in their separateness.' It is not in the world (Lao-Tsu's 'ten thousand things') that peace is to be found but in searching for the One within.

The anonymous author of *The Cloud of Unknowing* advises the use of a mantra as the best way to cut through discursive thinking and to bring the mind to heel:

> 'Take but a little word of one syllable: it is better than two, for the shorter it is, the more it accords with the Spirit. And such a word as this word "God", or "love". Choose which you will, or another, whichever appeals to you, of one syllable. And fasten this word to your heart, so that it never leaves you whatever befalls . . . With this word you shall smite down all manner of thoughts under the cloud of forgetting . . . And if you will hold fast to this purpose, be sure your thoughts will no longer trouble you . . .'

For the greatest of the English mystics, Dame Julian (a bhakti yogin if ever there was one), it is love and compassion that gets you there. And surrender, the let-go that comes only if you trust. In *The Showings of Divine Love* and *The Revelations of Divine Love*, this fourteenth-century anchoress describes a series of visions of Christ that came to her on 13 May 1373, in her cell built on to the wall of a Norwich church.

> 'At the same time that I saw this bodily sight of his bleeding head our Lord showed me . . . a little thing, the size of a hazelnut, which seemed to lie in the palm of my hand, and it was as round as any ball. I looked at it and thought, "What may this be?" and I was answered in a general way, thus: "It is all that is made." I wondered how long it could last for I thought it might fall suddenly to nothing, it was so little. And the answer came to my understanding, "It lasts and always shall last because God loves it, and just in this way everything has its being – through the love of God".'

In a later revelation, this message to relax and trust was reiterated: 'At one time our good Lord said: "All things shall be well"; and at another he said: "You shall see for yourself that all manner of thing shall be well."'

To allow ourselves to trust is essential for deep relaxation. We cannot let go – indeed it would be most unwise to – if we think there is a danger of falling. Interestingly, it has been found that the deepest fear of human beings, a primal dread remaining from our infant days, is of being dropped, of feeling totally without support. Perhaps one reason why prayer is comforting is that it reminds us that it makes us feel held. For if we trust that 'He's got the whole world in His hands', that includes us.

Unlike in the East, where seers are venerated, the Church has always seemed uneasy with its mystics and sometimes at a loss as to how to handle them. The author of *The Cloud of Unknowing* (probably a monk or a parish priest writing in the fourteenth century) chose to remain anonymous for fear of punishment for heresy; probably justifiably, in view of the treatment meted out by the Inquisition to Meister Eckhart, who escaped a post-humous excommunication (by a Pope who himself was later excommunicated) only by dying, disillusioned, at Avignon in 1328. From time to time mystics have continued to surface within the Roman Catholic Church: one thinks of Saint John of the Cross, the two Teresas (of Avila and Lisieux), the Quietists in late-seventeenth-century France, Saints Margaret Mary, Catherine Labouré and Bernadette . . . Most of them have had a hard time (at least initially) at the hands of the Establishment. This has also been to some extent true of the Catholic mystics of our own times, Teilhard de Chardin and Thomas Merton. Both of these – significantly, in view of the current trend – found much of their inspiration in the East (in Merton's case, especially from zen and his dialogue with D. T. Suzuki, who first made zen widely known in the West).

In the Russian Orthodox Church the mantra appears again as a device for stilling the mind. The 'Prayer of the Heart' (sometimes called the 'Jesus prayer') is described in the *Philokalia*, a collection of the writings of Greek and Byzantine spiritual teachers. The invocation 'Lord Jesus Christ, Have mercy on me' is to be repeated and timed to the rhythm of the breathing as one sits quietly alone.

> 'Say it, moving your lips gently, or simply say it with your mind. Try to set aside all other thoughts. Be calm, be patient, and repeat it very often.'

Here bhakti yoga and mantra yoga are integrated, just as they are in the recitation of litanies or the rosary by many Catholics today. An interesting point is that, in reciting the 'Jesus prayer', the devotee is advised to 'hold' his awareness in the heart, whereas the eastern tradition is to hold the mantra in the *hara*. One is reminded of Jung's observation that our Western psyches have been conditioned in a different way to those living in Eastern cultures. Perhaps after 2,000 years of Christianity it comes more naturally to us to centre our awareness in the heart *chakra* rather than in the *hara* when we relax into Alpha?

Perhaps it is appropriate to remind the reader before we leave this topic that our intention has been solely to learn from the insights of the mystics how to set aside the mind, not at all to evaluate the validity of their religious experience – or, indeed, anyone else's.

Auto-suggestion

Part of the Alpha Plan consists of changing one's mood by means of positive suggestions used in much the same way as mantras. In the 1920s auto-suggestion became very popular (in fact, something of a craze) on both sides of the Atlantic. The most famous champion of the beneficial effects of using this technique to influence the subconscious was Coué, and his most famous suggestion was '*Every day, in every way, I am getting better and better.*' He was using auto-suggestion with his patients at a clinic in Nancy and had a preference for this form of suggestion, since it was general enough to cover anything that might be troubling the patient. The suggestion was to be repeated to oneself several times slowly and with conviction, for the more one believes it, the truer it becomes. For the subconscious to be receptive to it one should be in a quiet frame of mind, preferably bordering on sleep (i.e. on waking in the morning or just before dropping off at night). Coué insisted that a passive attitude was essential for auto-suggestion to work: 'It is absolutely necessary to do it without effort. The use of the will must be entirely put aside.' A suggestion should always be framed in the positive form rather than the reverse, for example, '*I am feeling more and more relaxed*' instead of '*I am feeling less and less tense*'.

Psychotherapy

It is interesting that Freud came to formulate his theory of the subconscious after observing the hypnotist Mesmer in action.

As hypnotherapy, hypnosis is enjoying something of a revival today as a technique for changing unwanted behaviour, for example, stopping smoking or overcoming shyness. It is, however, mainly for some form of counselling that most people will probably go, or for the relief of emotional tension that has become unbearable.

It has often been suggested that the role of the confessional has been taken over by the consulting-room of the psycho-therapist. There, as in the confessional, relief from tension arising from inner conflict (for example, guilt) is (hopefully) achieved through the medium of words, the transmission of positive energy, and trust. Just as the confessor 'takes on' the sins of the penitent and absolves them through God's grace and forgiveness, so the modern therapist's 'unconditional positive regard' for the client and skill in working with the transference transforms neurotic suffering into what Freud called 'ordinary human suffering'. In the process it is very probable that much negativity will come to the surface, to be worked through and transformed, for it is seeing things (especially oneself) in a negative way that is the cause of much of the emotional tension that plagues the human race. According to their theoretical orientation, therapists will continue to disagree as to whether what really throws the spanner into the psyche's workings is 'unfinished business' to do with the Oedipal situation (Freudians), the inferiority complex (Adlerians), childish omnipotence and early object relationships (Kleinians), the integration of the shadow (Jungians) and so on. One wonders sometimes whether this is because the founders of these schools felt more at home working with psychic energy at different *chakra* levels, for example, Freud with the 1st and 2nd *chakras* (survival/sex), Adler and Klein with the 1st and 3rd (survival/ power) and Jung with the 5th and 6th (self-expression, creativity, inner vision). Playing with this model of the psyche, one wonders too whether the dynamics of the therapeutic process include the energizing of the higher centres for the recovery of feeling, authentic self-expression and insight (4th, 5th and 6th *chakras*). Whatever the model, absence of emotional conflict and being in a 'state of grace' would seem, experientially, to amount to the same thing.

Jung, especially, had much to say of relevance to the Alpha state, particularly of its creative potential which we shall be exploring later. He advocated the practice of using 'active imagination' when we are deeply relaxed, to tap into the Unconscious, which for him was not just a junk-yard (as Freud sometimes seems to be seeing the Subconscious), but the source of inspiration and direction. It was to this deep Alpha state (bordering on Theta) that Edison used to resort regularly for 'juice' while developing his inventions. (He used to avoid going too deep into Theta by holding a little ball in his hand, which, if he did drift off into sleep, would drop on the floor and wake him up again!)

Jung was fascinated by Eastern philosophy and was one of the early trail-blazers to this storehouse of experience of inner worlds. He used to enjoy showing his friends how to throw the *I Ching*, an ancient Chinese form of divination, about which he had written in an introduction to Wilhelm's classic translation of the hexagrams which interpret the meaning of the pattern of three coins (or jarrow sticks) dropped randomly on to a table. He had much to say about mandalas (symmetrical patterns, for example a cross or the Star of David) as symbols of wholeness – they had long been used (especially in Tibetan Buddhism) as objects of visualization and meditation for calming the mind. Jung foreshadowed what has since been discovered about the different functions of the left and right hemispheres of the brain, with his postulation of 'introversion' and 'extroversion' and of four psychological 'types' with 'superior' or 'inferior' functioning in thinking, feeling, sensing, intuition.

Progressive Relaxation

The importance of teaching a patient how to relax has been increasingly recognized by psychotherapists (and doctors). It is, for example, being used successfully in the treatment of phobics by desensitization, in which the patient learns to relax in situations which provoke a 'flight' response, experienced as panic.

Relaxation as a therapy was pioneered around 1910 by an American doctor, Edmund Jacobson. In his *Progressive Relaxation*, published in 1929, Dr Jacobson investigated the relationship between psychological states and skeletal muscle tension/relaxation. In *You Must Relax* (1938, revised edition 1976) he described in more popular form the by now well-known progressive relaxation of the 24 muscles and muscle groups, starting with the feet and ending with the forehead and scalp. This is achieved by first becoming aware of tension in the muscles − then learning to let go of it. With practice, even the slightest degree of tension anywhere in the body can be identified and eliminated − not by forcing, but simply by giving passive attention to the tension and allowing it to dissolve. Dr Jacobson points out that an active mind produces slight but measurable tension in the face and eye muscles, so incoming sense impressions are to be reduced as much as possible (for example by choosing a quiet environment and practising the technique with eyes closed).

Autogenic Training

Around the same time as Jacobson was developing progressive relaxation, a German neurologist, Dr Schultz, devised a therapy he called 'autogene training' because it was aimed at self-induced deep relaxation. In 1929 he said of it that it was developed out of his own experience of hypnosis, which he had used with his patients. Autogenics consists of six exercises ('orientations') which use auto-suggestion to influence some part of the body. The sequence is as follows:

1 'Right arm becoming heavy.'
2 'Right hand becoming warm.'

3   'Pulse calm and strong.'
4   'Breathing calm and regular.'
5   'Solar plexus warm.'
6   'Forehead pleasantly cool.'

As well as the hypnotic effect of these formulas, they serve also somewhat as mantras in that, if the mind starts wandering, attention has to be brought back to the words. (Once again this attention has to be *passive*, not at all the same as concentrated or effortful attention.) Since it has been found that the rest of the body does not necessarily relax automatically just because one part is relaxed, autogenics is now often combined with progressive relaxation of the whole body.

For more than 50 years autogenic training has been used in Central Europe for the relief of tension and psychosomatic disorders. It has become better known in Britain since the 1970s, due mainly to Dr Malcolm Carruthers, who brought the technique over from Canada.

'Alternative Therapies'

The current interest in 'new' therapies (some, like acupuncture, herbalism and homoeopathy, not at all new) is part of a growing health-consciousness and willingness to take responsibility for their own well-being on the part of more and more people today. We are now better informed about such topics as healthy eating, for example, about food additives, cholesterol, allergies, dietary fibre and vitamin and mineral requirements. Increasingly we are exploring alternatives to drugs and tranquillizers to help us to handle the stress and strain of modern living.

These 'alternative therapies' (or better, 'complementary therapies', since their role should really be seen as 'filling in the gaps' of orthodox medicine rather than supplanting the use of antibiotics or surgery in life-threatening medical conditions) include a whole range of different approaches to the promotion of well-being. Some of them, as we have said, are traditional and imported from the East, others have been developed in the last twenty years or so under the umbrella of humanistic psychology and the movement for holistic health. What they have in common are two basic assumptions:

1 That human beings cannot be divided into parts like a machine, but should be seen in 'holistic' terms, i.e. what happens in the body affects mental and emotional states and vice versa.

2 That well-being and 'dis-ease' (on whichever level it manifests) is a function of the whole organism and is directly related to its changing energy-states, e.g. high or low, flowing or 'blocked'.

The relationship between high energy and good health has been demonstrated in Kirlian photography. This system, invented by a Russian electrician named Semyon Kirlian, actually photographs the 'aura' of a person's energy field, which shows up as patterns and colours, for example round a hand placed on the aluminium plate to which a high-frequency field is delivered. Kirlian discovered that when he was ill his energy field registered as blurred and faint. That of his wife Valentina, however, who was well, remained bright and clear. Research in Russia and, in the 1970s, in the West, has managed to use Kirlian photography to successfully diagnose certain illnesses before the onset of symptoms.

Some 'alternative' therapies seek to change a person's mental or feeling state by working directly on or through the body, for example acupuncture, homoeopathy, bioenergetics, massage (including *shiatsu*), rolfing, kinesiology, Alexander Technique, aromatherapy, Bach flower remedies, and, of course, all forms of dieting, including macrobiotics. Others, like gestalt, co-counselling, encounter and Voice Dialogue, will tackle 'unfinished business' (emotional hangups and unresolved personal and interpersonal conflicts from the past which make us tense and less able to respond objectively and appropriately to present situations). Yet others use a variety of techniques to control the mind's creative potential and free us from its tendency to control *us*, too often in a negative way.

Among these 'enlightenment programmes' one would include psychosynthesis, *est*, Silva Mind Control and Neuro-Linguistic Programming (NLP). One of the features of what in the sixties and seventies used to be called the 'Growth Movement' (i.e. the Movement for Human Potential and Personal Growth) has been the emergence of 'energy masters' who have from their own experience devised new, non-traditional pathways to the Alpha state, and whose charisma has attracted large followings. Among these are Jose Silva, Werner Erhard, and Michael Barnett.

Visualization

One of the most powerful techniques used in many of these new therapies for the transformation of both psychic and physiological states has been guided fantasy or visualization. That imagining certain things affects the way we feel is not a new idea. We have seen this dynamic at work in the Buddhist *metta* meditation. In ordinary conversation we say 'That's a happy thought' or 'What a gloomy thought!' This is in fact a sort of shorthand. For what we really are saying is 'Thinking about this makes me *feel* good (or depressed).' It has now been scientifically proven that these emotional reactions to thoughts in turn can affect the *body's* processes, often in dramatic ways.

Measurements of various bodily functions have been correlated with emotional states in a system called 'sentic cycles' devised by Dr Manfred Clynes, a psychophysiological researcher. These show clearly that negativity churns up not only the mind and emotions, but the body as well. Dr Clynes gets his subjects to work themselves up into an emotional state by imagining situations likely to induce it. The prescribed emotions ('sentic states') in the required sequence (a 'sentic circle') are:

no emotion
anger
hate
grief
love
sex
joy
reverence

At a given signal while in each of these states the subject presses what looks rather like a piano key, which records the finger pressure on to a chart. At the same time, the subject's bodily functions are also being monitored and recorded. Predictable physiological changes occur according to each emotional state. With Dr Clynes's subjects, changes indicating relaxation were noted often in the case of 'reverence', 'love' and (surprisingly) 'grief'. The opposite was most markedly the case with 'anger' and 'hate'.

The most dramatic demonstrations of the effects on the body of deliberately thinking positively about it have come from America, where they have been used (in conjunction with orthodox medical treatment) for healing. Remissions from cancer and, more recently, from Kaposi's sarcoma and other A I D S-related diseases have been clinically confirmed in some well-documented cases (for example, Louis Nassaney). Following the heartening results achieved at the Cancer Counselling and Research Center in Texas by Dr Carl Simonton and Stephanie Matthews-Simonton (a survival rate twice the national norm and many remissions or total cures), visualization techniques are now also being used in Britain at Cancer Help Centres. If visualization can affect (in some cases, not all) the course of intractable organic disease in this way, how much easier it must be for it to help to relax muscle tension.

Biofeedback

The latest development in the 'technology of relaxation' has been biofeedback. First developed in America in the 1960s by medical scientists, biofeedback instruments are designed to give immediate 'feedback' about one's state of tension or relaxation by monitoring electrical activity in muscles (EMG), skin resistance to electricity (ESR) or brainwave rhythms (EEG). Using these electronic machines which are capable of detecting the slightest tension, one realizes how often one thinks one is relaxed and isn't (or that one can always go deeper into relaxation). More usefully, biofeedback facilitates the acquisition of control of the 'relaxation response', processes normally operated only by the autonomic nervous system (i.e. automatically by the body). By keeping an eye on the monitor and 'playing' with how one feels, one learns by trial and error the subtle internal and subjective ways of affecting muscle tension, heart rate, and blood pressure. When biofeedback machines become less expensive they should be more widely available, to the advantage not only of sufferers from tension and anxiety states, migraine, high blood pressure and similar conditions, but of anyone interested in learning to relax more deeply for whatever reason. In Australia, for example, coach Peter Keller trained Olympic athletes in the art of effortless performance by using ESR.

Biofeedback machines can now also measure brainwave activity and show how it varies depending on what you do and what you think about, for example, C. Maxwell Cade's 'Mind Mirror'. Cade brought to the study of brainwaves excellent credentials, being a Fellow of the Royal Society of Medicine and having trained in zen with a zen master. In 1968, in his capacity of chief medical adviser to a large company, he became interested in investigating the brainwaves that he saw on EEG tracings of patients in hospitals. By the early seventies he was experimenting with the use of a simple EEG machine, and in 1974 he studied the brainwave activity of healers, who seemed to be producing waves symmetrically from both hemispheres.

At about this time he met an engineer, Geoffrey Blundell, who designed the Mind Mirror, a two-channel portable machine which could analyse signals from the left and right hemispheres of the brain and display them on a monitor as a pattern of little red lights. The prototype was first used on one of Cade's courses

Diagram 1

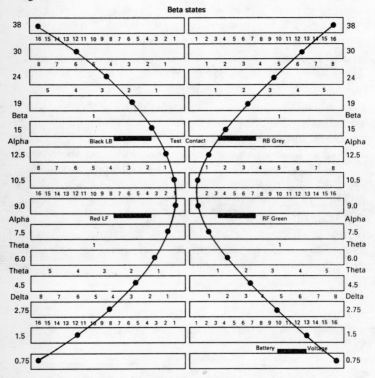

in meditation and relaxation in June 1976, and the perfected model is still being used today on similar courses run by Cade's widow in London.

Examples of brainwave patterns that have been recorded on a cassette (rather than being photographed because of the fluidity of the waves as they appear on the Mind Mirror) are given here and overleaf. When there is no signal, all the lights line up at the centre of the display. The diagrams reproduced show different brainwave patterns that go with different states of mind, feeling and movement. The numbers down the outside of

Diagram 2

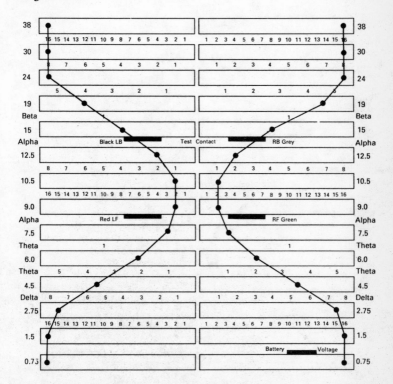

the diagrams show the frequency, ranging from 38 Hz in Beta down to 0.75 in Delta. The small numbers along the horizontal lines indicate the amplitude of the signal (the 1–16 figures measured in millionths of a volt). Movement of the position of the red light away from the centre towards the left shows the degree of left hemisphere activity, and movement towards the right, activity of the right hemisphere.

It will be apparent from these diagrams that when we talk about 'being in an Alpha state' we really mean 'producing predominantly Alpha waves', for the other frequencies will be

Diagram 3

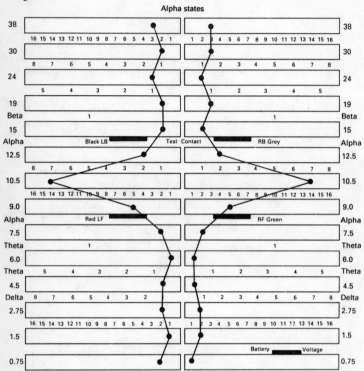

Alpha states

there also, but much diminished in amplitude. The amount of Beta activity present will depend on how much attention is being focused on the outside world.

'The stability and relative levels will vary from subject to subject and they are likely to be symmetrical if he or she

is naturally calm or has achieved a minimum of training in mental relaxation or in meditation.' (Geoffrey G.
Blundell, *The Meaning of EEG*)

Diagrams 1 and 2 show 'Alpha blocking', the apprehensive or
unsure response of the average person to first being connected

Diagram 4

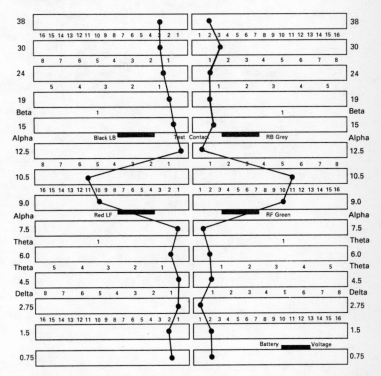

to a Mind Mirror. Beta is predominant in both, the subject in
diagram 2 producing the excessive Beta typical of the 'fight or
flight' response. Diagrams 3 and 4 show Alpha states in which
the subject has 'switched off' involvement with the external
world and is experiencing the 'relaxation response'.

PART TWO

THE ALPHA PLAN

6

PATHWAYS TO ALPHA

We must now bring the approaches to deep psychophysical relaxation of both East and West together to see how they are combined in the Alpha Plan for Total Relaxation.

Whatever their concept of the goal, each of the disciplines we looked at in the last two chapters was concerned with one or more of five pathways to a state characterized by a predominance of Alpha brain activity. These pathways were:

1   RELAXING FROM 'DOING'
2   TRANSFORMING NEGATIVE EMOTIONS
3   CONTROLLING THE MIND
4   CENTRING AWARENESS IN THE BODY
5   BEING IN THE 'HERE AND NOW'

There is a certain amount of overlap, of course, since feelings, mind and body are not separate. To relax the body, for example, will make the mind start to slow down, and vice versa. Doing either makes one feel good. Different approaches are different 'ways in' to Alpha, have different theoretical models, use different terminology. But the same techniques keep on recurring over and over. These are:

> passive awareness
> attention to breathing
> mantras
> attention to the body
> auto-suggestion

    visualization

    faith, trust, surrender

Using any one of these techniques on its own helps us relax by setting us on to one of the five pathways listed above, each of which leads us eventually down out of Beta into Alpha. But sometimes these ways, followed on their own, can be long and arduous, necessitating much practice before the goal is reached, as in yoga and meditation. Often, too, one has to pay teachers or therapists, or sign up for courses in order to learn the necessary technique, for example, in biofeedback or autogenics.

The Alpha Plan is an autogenic (i.e. self-help) short-cut to deep and total relaxation which integrates *all* the pathways into a new and unique synthesis that 'gets you there' whenever you want, whenever you need, whenever you have time. The Plan is flexible, takes only as much time as you have – and costs no money. And, most important of all, it works because each of its five stages is in itself a pathway to Alpha that has been validated, as we have seen, by the experience of both ancient tradition and modern scientific research.

Here, once again, are the five pathways which, taken in succession, make up the five stages of the Alpha Plan for Total Relaxation. The sequence given is the one that, in the author's own experience, flows most naturally, and is therefore the one he uses in his courses in relaxation. But, as we have said, the Plan is flexible and readers will no doubt experiment with the order of the stages to find which sequence suits them best. This time they are listed slightly differently, with a view to making each more meaningful in terms of what each state feels like, what it is aiming at, and, possibly, as a mantra to be used to help in attaining it. With each stage is suggested the most appropriate technique to be used for that stage.

THE ALPHA PLAN: THE FIVE STAGES

STAGE	PATHWAY	TECHNIQUE
1	Senses relaxed	Passive awareness
2	Feelings positive	Auto-suggestion or visualization
3	Mind slowing down	Breathing + Mantra
4	Body relaxing	Body scanning
5	Letting go	Allowing, trusting

Comments

We should be in a comfortable position, preferably lying down, with eyes closed and, if desired, wearing some sort of blindfold to cut out as much light as possible. The room should be as quiet as possible and we should be sure that we will not be disturbed for at least half an hour. Loose clothing should be worn (no shoes), and enough of it to ensure we don't feel cold.

STAGE 1: 'SENSES RELAXED'

This is really what we mean colloquially when we talk of 'switching off' or 'unwinding'. It involves ceasing any form of physical activity, relaxing the concentration and allowing oneself to 'be here now' in a totally passive way. This stage counteracts the effects of sensory overload from outside stimuli, or fatigue from intense concentration or overdoing and the contraction of awareness that goes with it. We simply start to withdraw energy from the outside world by relaxing our attention from it and our involvement in it and allowing ourselves to be as passive as we can.

STAGE 2: 'FEELINGS POSITIVE'

It is possible to be in Alpha when we are merely feeling 'neutral' as well as when we are feeling 'good'. It is not possible, however, to get out of Beta until any negativity has been dispersed, which is why, for example, it is so hard to get to sleep if we are worried or angry. This stage, therefore, is about using verbal formulas or imagination to reassure ourselves (at least for the time being) that we are safe enough to allow ourselves to relax, or to defuse any negative feelings we may be dwelling on that otherwise will keep us tense.

STAGE 3: 'MIND SLOWING DOWN'

Getting down from Beta wavelengths to Alpha is very much about slowing down the mind's activity. Even if we are not carrying negativity around with us and have also 'switched off' and stopped 'doing', the mind will have its own momentum and go on running its own 'home movies'. The way to slow it down is not to fight it but to give it something to play with, rather as one would distract a fractious child with a toy. Giving passive attention to breathing together with repetition of a mantra serves this purpose of focusing the mind into one-pointedness, of putting a brake on its tendency to go off in all directions or to be obsessed with one idea. By and by, if we do not get caught up in linear thinking but merely allow thoughts to be there without feeding them attention, energy starts to leave the head and trickle down into the body.

STAGE 4: 'BODY RELAXING'

When we start to become aware of body sensations it is time to go on to this stage. We call it 'Body Relaxing' rather than 'Body Relaxed' because the body can always relax *more*. Once our awareness is centred in the body, keeping it there is an effective silencer of the mind, for our attention cannot be in two places at once, i.e. either we are feeling or we are thinking. So this stage is about feeling 'from the inside' what is going on in your body and 'staying with' whatever that is from moment to moment. To begin with (especially if you happen to be a 'thinking' type living very much in your head) you may have to heighten your awareness of your body by progressively relaxing it from toes to scalp. With practice you will be able simply to give passive attention with body-scanning, i.e. letting your attention roam freely wherever it is attracted by sensations that arise anywhere in the body. If nothing is happening then attention should be centred either in the *hara* (see page 40) or in the heart. Simply giving attention to the body in this way is to relax it, for, as we have said elsewhere, body awareness and relaxation are the same.

STAGE 5: 'LETTING GO'

'Letting go' is not only the last stage of the Alpha Plan but also the goal – a state of total relaxation from mental, emotional or muscular tension that can be enjoyed for as long as you wish or have time for. This final stage also incorporates the other stages in the sense that they will be continuing at the same time. In other words, we will continue just giving passive awareness to outside sounds and body sensations, watching thoughts, and, if the latter are intrusive, returning to counting the breath or repeating a mantra. Stage 5 is the ultimate in 'non-doing' in the 'here and now', a passive wakefulness harnessed to a sleeping body. The less movement of any kind there is, the deeper we go into the Alpha state and into Theta and the borders of sleep. If you definitely do not want to doze off, then you should follow the Alpha Plan sitting, rather than lying down. However, if you do doze off, when you come to again you will feel refreshed at a very deep level and as energized as if you had had a good night's sleep.

Timing

Initially, you should arrange not to be disturbed for a minimum of half an hour to relax through the five stages of the Alpha Plan. These will probably apportion themselves out as follows:

Stage 1: Senses Relaxed (5 minutes)
Stage 2: Feelings Positive (5 minutes)
Stage 3: Mind Slowing Down (5 minutes)
Stage 4: Body Relaxing (10 minutes)
Stage 5: Letting Go (ad lib)

Timing of each stage once again is necessarily flexible, depending on whether your need to relax is predominantly from sensory overload, emotional tension, over-concentration or bodily fatigue. For example, apportion more time to Stage 1 for 'coming down' from, say, a shopping trip to the sales or a long drive, and to 'switch off' from having had to put out so much energy through the eyes and to take in so much information through the senses. If you are more aware of feeling uptight from emotional tension, Stage 2 will need more time to soothe ruffled feelings and calm you down. Similarly with Stage 3, if your mind is buzzing after concentrating hard – studying, for example. Stage 4 takes longer naturally than the preceding stages because the more awareness you give to the body, the deeper you go into a relaxed state. If what you are most in touch with when you start the Alpha Plan is muscular fatigue, then the body will clamour for your attention anyway as soon as you lie down. The time you allot to the last stage is optional, but be aware if you tend to cut it short when you don't need to because you are unused to giving good things to yourself, or feel uncomfortable with surrendering control, blissful though letting go of it is.

Allow a few minutes for coming out of low Alpha in an unhurried way, otherwise the effect will be as jarring as waking up in the morning and having to rush out of bed because you realize you have overslept. How to do this will be explained in the next chapter, together with a stage by stage run-down. Later chapters will explore what can be done about resistance to relaxing that might be encountered in any stage, and also how the Plan can be adapted to handle the stresses and strains of your working day.

Once you get confidence with using these pathways to Alpha you will begin to take charge of your own 'relaxation response' and may modify the sequence of the stages to match your own rhythms and requirements. Look at the Alpha Plan, therefore, as a prototype (no pun intended!) for your own version of the five stages.

The Alpha Spiral

It may help to visualize the Alpha Plan as a spiral staircase (rather like a fire escape) leading down from Beta to Alpha (as in the illustration given on page 75). Think of each of the five stages as a 'landing stage' on the way down, a platform where you rest for a while before continuing to descend. Each landing stage has a lamp, which you switch on when you reach it and leave on when you move on so that it lights your way down to the next landing stage. By the time you reach the bottom, all the lights should still be on. If not, you may have to go back and re-light it. What this means in practice is that if totally letting go in the last stage is being blocked by any form of tightening up again (usually from disturbing thoughts or sense-impressions), you will have to handle these with the appropriate techniques again in the same way as you did first time round. 'All lights on' by Stage 5 means senses *remaining* relaxed, feelings *still* positive or neutral, mind *continuing* to slow down, body becoming *more and more* relaxed . . .

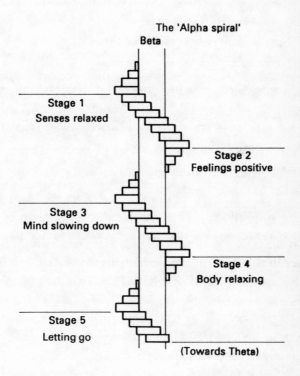

7

THE ALPHA PLAN FOR TOTAL RELAXATION

ESSENTIAL PREPARATIONS

1 Withdraw to a quiet room.

2 Make sure you will not be disturbed for at least half an hour. (Set the alarm if you definitely do not want to fall asleep or have to be somewhere immediately after your deep relaxation session.)

3 Wear loose-fitting clothing (no shoes) and ensure that you will not feel cold.

4 Make yourself very comfortable, either lying down or sitting. You are less likely to fall asleep if you sit rather than lie.

5 Have the *intention* to relax. Just saying to yourself 'This time is for me to relax as deeply as I can' will be enough to programme yourself.

OPTIONAL PREPARATIONS

1 Take a warm shower or bath.

2 Put on soft, soothing background music (preferably Baroque, 'New Age', meditation music or a tape of sounds of nature, e.g. the sea, running water or birdsong).*

3 Wear a blindfold.

* Suitable tapes are available from Mysteries, 9 Monmouth Street, Covent Garden, London W C 2.

STAGE 1: 'SENSES RELAXED'

PURPOSE

To relax from concentration and sensory overload.

TECHNIQUE

Expanding awareness of the here and now.

1   Take a few slow, deep breaths.

2   Become aware of tension around the eyes. Unfocus them (eyes closed) until they feel very 'soft'.

3   Listen passively to sounds from the outside that are reaching you. Just allow them to be there, without trying to identify them. After a few minutes of this 'tuning in' move on to:

STAGE 2: 'FEELINGS POSITIVE'

PURPOSE

To feel safe and calm enough to let go of negativity (at least temporarily).

TECHNIQUE

Dwelling on positive thought-forms.

One or both of the following, depending on how emotionally tense you are feeling:

1   Repeat several times, silently and slowly, a phrase or sentence which reassures you about something that is

worrying, disturbing or upsetting you. Examples of suggestions are given in the next chapter. Until you have worked
out your own, use Coué's favourite 'all-rounder': *'Every day,
in every way, I'm getting better and better'*.

and/or

2 Enjoy a fantasy about being where you would most like to
be right now. Visualize a place (or a situation) where you
feel totally safe, loved and supported, free from worry and
tension. Imagine yourself relaxing there and feeling totally
contented. Examples of visualizations are given in the next
chapter. If you have no particular preference, why not enjoy
returning to your favourite beach (or creating your ideal
one)? How would it feel to be basking in hot sunshine right
now? Imagine the sound of waves lapping the shore, of
sea-birds wheeling overhead in the clear blue sky . . . Feel
the warm sand under your feet . . . Smell the fragrance of
the suntan lotion on your body (or on that of a beautiful
friend lying next to you) . . . Relax and enjoy this treat you
are giving yourself.

Your mind will probably be resisting giving up its preoccupations with your problems and the 'real world'. If unwanted
thoughts keep intruding on your fantasy move on to:

STAGE 3: 'MIND SLOWING DOWN'

PURPOSE

To get some peace from the 'monkey mind'.

Focusing the thoughts on something calming and repetitive.

1   Become aware of your breathing. Without changing it in any way, simply count after each exhalation: 'ONE' ... (breathe in ... breathe out ...) 'TWO' ... (breathe in ... breathe out ...) 'THREE' ... up to 'TEN' and then start another round with 'ONE' ...

2   After a few rounds of counting in this way, substitute a mantra for the number after each exhalation. Choose a word that has calming associations for you (examples of soothing mantras are given in the next chapter). In the meantime you could simply use the word 'RELAX' as a mantra after each exhalation.

As the mind slows down, you will start to become aware of sensations in your body. This is the time to move on to:

STAGE 4: 'BODY RELAXING'

PURPOSE

To get the muscles to let go of 'holding' so as to experience progressively deeper levels of body relaxation.

TECHNIQUE

Scanning the body with passive awareness and allowing yourself really to *feel* tension wherever it exists.

Start with the big toe of the left foot. Without moving it, let your attention *feel it from the inside*, its size and shape ... From there, after 10 seconds or so, let your attention roam over the toes of the left foot in turn (once again without twiddling them), just being as aware of them as you can, one after the other.

Now feel the rest of the left foot in turn: the heel resting on the floor or mattress, the sensitive sole, the hard bones on top of the instep. Take your time. Now feel the weight of the whole foot, and how it is supported for you. Imagine it as getting heavier and sinking downwards . . . Move on now to the left ankle. Feel 'from the inside' its shape and the hardness of the bones . . . Move upwards to the calf muscle and feel whether it is tense or relaxed . . . Imagine it expanding and getting softer, heavier . . . Feel the kneecap, its shape, size, hardness – and the soft area behind it . . . and the length and hardness of the shin. Become aware of your left thigh, front and back, and the difference in tension in each part.

Now let your awareness scan the whole of the left leg and foot. Feel it getting heavier, and how much heavier and more relaxed it feels than the right leg and foot . . . Now feel as if you are letting go of your left leg. Repeat the whole sequence with your right foot and right leg, starting from the toes as before.

When both legs are totally relaxed, allow yourself to become aware in turn of the other parts of your body, spending as much time on each part as you need before moving on. With each part

(a) feel it first 'from the inside', its size and shape;
(b) feel how relaxed or tense it is – and 'relax into the tension';

(c) imagine it getting heavier, softer, expanding;
(d) let go of it.

Continue with the following sequence:

> buttocks;
> anus and genitals;
> lower back;
> spine;
> shoulders;
> left arm (upper, elbow, forearm, wrist);
> left hand (palm, back, thumb, fingers);
> right arm (upper, elbow, forearm, wrist);
> right hand (palm, back, thumb, fingers);
> belly (allow this to feel as if it is opening up);
> chest (breathe slow and deep into the heart area, sighing – feel that you are cleansing and energizing the heart);
> Feel the whole weight of your torso – and let it get heavier, expanding, sinking down;
> Lastly, allow yourself really to feel all the tension that comes with having to 'face the world' (jaw, mouth, eyes) and 'be in your head' so much (scalp) – and let go of it.

STAGE 5: 'LETTING GO'

PURPOSE

Total relaxation

TECHNIQUE

Allowing yourself to relax more and more deeply into the body while keeping a totally passive, allowing attitude to all sense impressions or 'inner movement', i.e. thoughts or feelings. This stage, even more than the preceding stages, is one of 'allowing' rather than 'doing', of 'letting it happen'. 'It' is the bliss of total relaxation that comes with surrender.

COMING OUT OF ALPHA: Before resuming normal activity give yourself a few minutes to ground yourself again to avoid feeling jarred. Here are some ways to do this:

(a) opening your eyes and looking around the room;
(b) getting up slowly;
(c) feeling your feet on the floor;
(d) stretching;
(e) massaging your hands.

Summary of the Alpha Plan

STAGE 1: EYES CLOSED, UNFOCUSED, 'SOFT', 'JUST LISTENING' (5 minutes)

STAGE 2: AUTO-SUGGESTION and/or VISUALIZATION (5 minutes)

STAGE 3: COUNTING THE BREATH + MANTRA (5 minutes)

STAGE 4: BODY SCANNING (10 minutes)

STAGE 5: TOTAL PASSIVITY (ad lib)

GROUNDING: (2 minutes)

The suggested timing is, remember, flexible. Play with it.

8

NOTES AND REMINDERS

General

1 The goal of the Alpha Plan is reached when you are as blissfully relaxed as you want to be. See the stages of the Plan merely as devices to get you there, not as ends in themselves. It may not be necessary to work through all the stages before total 'let-go' starts happening – it depends on how tense you were before you started the process. It can happen at any stage. The flexibility of the Plan also allows you to go only as deep into relaxation as you want to – or feel comfortable with.

2 The totally relaxed state cannot be attained by any form of doing (including thinking). As we have seen, effort of any kind keeps us in Beta. 'Trying to relax' is like jabbing at the Daruma doll to make it stand still, or like stirring up the bottom of a muddy pool with a stick to make the water clear again. What we should rather be doing is waiting patiently, watching, not interfering with the natural tendency of things to come to rest. Think of each stage, therefore, not as '*making* you relax', but as helping you get out of the way of relaxation happening. All you are doing is slowing down, switching off, unwinding, so you can eventually get to the point where it is possible just to let go of 'holding on' to tension, whether mental, emotional or muscular. The Alpha Plan is thus a *via negativa*, a removing of the barrier to just 'sitting quietly, doing nothing' – which includes linear thinking – and allowing the 'natural state of the mind' (Alpha) to establish itself again.

3 This barrier to 'non-doing' consists of our accumulated

tension (mental, emotional or bodily) and our restlessness, the compulsive 'urge to do'. These two are aspects of the same phenomenon: the tenser you are, the more you want to do, and the more you feel you have to do, the more you tense up. The Alpha Plan gets us out of this vicious circle by withdrawing energy from making ourselves tense and by watching our own restlessness. In Stages 1–4 we practise withdrawing energy in turn from

~ *active* involvement with the outside world;
~ concentrating;
~ dwelling on negative thoughts and feelings;
~ following *any* particular train of thought;
~ tightening up the body.

When mental, emotional and physical tension have been dispersed in this way, all that is left is total relaxation.

4 The most passive mode possible for an awake human being is to be just an observer. 'Just watching' (or 'witnessing' as it is called in meditation) is the only opposite there is of 'doing'. This 'passive awareness', giving unforced attention, is the most important of all the techniques that make up the Alpha Plan, for it is needed in all five stages. The overriding importance of a passive attitude was stressed in his pioneering book *The Relaxation Response* by Dr Herbert Benson (the first to coin this phrase). The other factors he considered significant were a quiet environment, a 'mental device' and a comfortable position.

5 Tension is dispersed not by fighting it (which would make us more tense) but by surrendering to it, relaxing into it. We try to become aware of where exactly we are tense and how much – and feel the quality of this tension as much as we can. The more we 'stay with it', the more it melts. Tension contracts, makes us 'uptight'. Awareness expands, 'loosens us up'. It is like a searchlight that disperses the darkness of tension simply by its presence.

Stage 1: 'Eyes Closed, Unfocused, Soft – Just Listening'

This stage starts the unwinding process after being caught up in the 'ten thousand things' – the preoccupations, problems, relating, changing situations and sensory stimulation that make up an ordinary working day for most of us. We withdraw into ourselves from active participation in the outer world, at least for a while, to give ourselves a well-earned rest from it and to refresh our jaded senses. Outside our windows the noise and bustle go on, but we just let it be there while we take a break from the treadmill or the rat race. Right now there is no one we need to relate to, nothing we need to do, look at, or hear – which is why we have

(a) withdrawn into our own space;
(b) made ourself comfortable;
(c) 'switched off' our eyes;
(d) given up for the moment being interested in what's going on 'out there' as conveyed to us by the sound of it. However 'it' sounds out there from moment to moment (a passing car, a police siren, voices, a dog barking or whatever), treat all the sounds in the same way – with indifference. Or, as Tibetan Buddhists say, 'Hear all sounds as mantras.'

Stage 2: Auto-suggestion and/or Visualization

In Stage 2 we appear to be abandoning the passivity of Stage 1. But in fact this is not so. Remember Coué's insistence that a passive attitude is essential for auto-suggestion to work: 'It is absolutely necessary to do it without effort. The use of the will must be entirely put aside.' We must *receive* our own suggestions with the same receptivity as if they were being made to us by somebody else who, we trust, knows better than ourselves.

Similarly, in the case of visualization, the most important aspect is not so much the actual content of the 'mind video' you select (so long as it is enjoyable and soothing), as getting the 'feel' of actually participating in it into your body – and in order to experience this feeling you have to move out of the 'active' left brain hemisphere into the 'passive' right hemisphere. In other words, doing a visualization is like watching a movie – you just relax and enjoy the action. Below are some examples of auto-suggestion affirmations and visualizations that you might like to use from time to time where appropriate, as well, of course, as making up your own.

Remember that affirmations used in auto-suggestion:

(a) should always be framed in the affirmative form (e.g. *I am feeling more and more relaxed* NOT *I am feeling less and less tense*);

(b) should be a statement which is exactly the opposite of the negative way you have been thinking or feeling;

(c) should be repeated several times, silently, passively – and with total suspension of disbelief. After all, you are merely exercising your choice to be how you want to be.

Examples of affirmations (and the type of negativity they counteract)

> *Every moment that passes I am feeling fitter and stronger* (if anxious about health).
>
> *I feel totally lovable just the way I am* (if feeling bad about yourself).
>
> *I forgive X for . . . with all my heart and wish (him, her) well* (if feeling angry or hurt).
>
> *I feel totally supported by Life* (if feeling insecure, e.g. about money).
>
> *The whole world is my family and my home* (if feeling lonely, alienated, isolated).
>
> *I feel peace, joy and love* (if depressed).
>
> *This too shall pass* (if feeling grief at loss, e.g. bereavement).
>
> *I forgive myself for . . .* (if blaming yourself for not being perfect).
>
> *I am giving more and more to myself right now* (if feeling un-nourished).

I have all the time and space I need right now (if feeling under
   pressure).

   Carry on repeating the affirmation until you have the feeling
it carries 'in your bones'. Make it as 'on target' as possible, i.e.
specifically geared to what is or has been bothering you.

Visualizations

When making a visualization remember to:

(a) keep it loving, caring and positive, not only towards your-
     self but about any others you include in the visualization as
     well;
(b) include as much detail as you can to make it more vivid;
(c) continue with it until you have the feeling in your body
     that what you are imagining has actually occurred.

Getting this feeling into your body is the most important part of
the visualization process. If you find visualization difficult, don't
worry. It is enough just to *feel* the positive energy, either by
auto-suggestion or by recalling the feeling content of, for
example, sunbathing on a beach or enjoying the fragrance
and freshness of a garden on a summer's day.

Examples of visualizations

Your favourite garden (calming if feeling stressed)

   Where is it?
   How is it laid out: formal, landscaped, a wilderness?
   What flowers, shrubs, trees can you see growing there?
   What colours are most prominent and where?
   What sounds are you aware of (e.g. running water, bees
      buzzing, a plane droning high overhead . . .)
   What features of the garden do you particularly like?
   Add any other ones that you wish e.g. a fountain,
      fishpond, gazebo, peacocks . . .

Where are you in your garden and how could you be
enjoying it most (strolling, sunbathing on the grass,
smelling the flowers, having afternoon tea with friends,
dozing in a deckchair . . .)?
How does it feel to be in this garden?
Allow yourself to savour this feeling as vividly as you can.

'No problems' (if anxious, worried or insecure)
Imagine that a problem that has been worrying you or a
situation that has been upsetting you has been resolved
to your total satisfaction.
How are you celebrating your good fortune?
Who are you sharing it with?
How are you expressing your relief and gratitude?
How does it feel to be without problems?
Allow this feeling to permeate your body. Enjoy it.

'Metta' (for resentment of others, for example, after
quarrelling)
This Buddhist visualization is described on pages 37–8.

'Meditating on the opposite'
Similar to *Metta*, this is an effective mood-changer. Use this
technique also when you cannot really pinpoint any
specific reason why you should be feeling 'down' – for
example, a quarrel, loss, financial or health worry – but
you just do. For example, if feeling vaguely depressed,
try to remember happier times and to recall how you felt
then. If feeling sorry for yourself, neglected, perhaps, or
impoverished, literally 'count your blessings' by reminding yourself of how many 'goodies' you have that
you take for granted like health, absence of pain, family,
nourishing relationships and (unlike many in this
world), a roof over your head and knowing where the
next meal is coming from . . .

Stage 3: Counting the Breath + Mantra

You do not need to alter the rate or depth of your breathing in any way. Just carry on breathing as you normally do, through the nostrils, but become aware that breathing is happening. It helps to avoid distraction by letting your attention rest on the tip of your nose.

Start counting silently after each exhalation:

'ONE' . . . 'TWO' . . . 'THREE', starting again when you reach 'TEN' with 'ONE' . . . 'TWO' . . . etc. Once you are centred without distraction in counting, start silently to repeat a mantra of your choice after each exhalation instead of the number. Benson reported that tests at the Thorndike Memorial Laboratory at Harvard established that the physiological changes associated with the deep relaxation occurred whatever the type of verbal formula used. So don't be too concerned at finding the 'right' mantra: just choose a word of few syllables that feels relaxing and centring for you and has no disturbing associations. Here are a few suggestions you might like to try:

'RELAX(ING)'
'PEACE(FUL)'
'NOW'
'NOW-HERE' (or 'NO-WHERE')
'(YOUR OWN NAME)'
'LOVE'

As you repeat the word, feel as if it is resonating in the centre of your body, whether you experience this centre to be your *hara* (see page 40) or your heart. Since energy follows attention, this will help to ground you in the body as well as facilitating slowing down thinking.

Stage 4: Body Scanning

Giving passive awareness to the body is the most important stage in the Alpha Plan, for here technique and the goal – total relaxation – begin to merge. This is because, as we continue to emphasize, to be thus 'in the body' is to be present-centred and out of the mind – which is the relaxed state. As the Founder of Gestalt Therapy put it, we have to 'lose our mind and come to our senses'.

Remember that 'we' are where our attention is: experientially, subjectively, nothing exists except what we are aware of at this moment. Our attention, for most of the day, is having to be 'out there' in the environment (and our consciousness, therefore, in Beta states) – and necessarily so if we are to survive and relate. But what this means is that most of us, most of the time, are unaware of our bodies – and are therefore also unaware of just how much tension they are accumulating in the course of an average working day, how often the 'fight, flight or freeze' response is being activated.

Most people tend to be more in touch with their thoughts and feelings about what is happening outside them than with their body sensations, except when these intrude into awareness, for example, when we get a headache, toothache or indigestion, when we are in the bathroom, or making love. This is why we have had to 'clear the decks' in the first three stages of the Alpha Plan to allow for body awareness to surface in Stage 4. Having withdrawn energy from concern with the environment and from the feelings and thoughts churned up by relating to it, we are now ready to 'come home' and relax, not only in a quiet room, but inside the body in which we live.

When you first start doing the Alpha Plan it will probably be necessary in Stage 4 to scan your body from toes to scalp in the sequence described on pages 79–81, in order to become aware of where you are 'holding', i.e. which sets of muscles are contracted, tense. With practice in passive awareness you will soon be able to 'zone in' straight away to where the tension is in any part of your body as soon as you start to give attention to body sensations. If you are very passive and merely scan 'from the inside' you will feel the 'tight spots' one after the other. It is almost as if they are asking for your attention to be told whether they can 'stand at ease' (just as, sometimes, in the form of pain, they urge us to do or stop doing something). This you do, first by 'hearing' them (i.e. experiencing their contracted state), then by 'dismissing' them (i.e. by allowing relaxation/expansion to happen). If you wish, you can use a mantra as a command to each part to relax.

Stage 5: Total Passivity

The more passive you can allow your awareness to be and the more you can allow it to sink into the body, the more totally relaxed you will be feeling by this last stage of the Alpha Plan. As they say in zen, 'Let the mind have no abiding-place.' In other words, just be there and allow yourself to feel whatever you are feeling. If, in our image of the landing-stages of the fire-escape at the end of Chapter 6, 'all the lights are still on', what you will be experiencing is a blissfully sleeping body and a free-floating awareness. *This combination can only come about by the use of a 'meditative technique', of which the Alpha Plan is one.*

What to do, however, if total relaxation is not happening? The first thing is to take responsibility for your resistance to letting go of your tension and to become aware of what this is about. In terms of our 'landing lights' model, to which level (i.e. stage of the Alpha Plan) do you have to return to bring the light of awareness to dispel the murkiness of tension? Where is the movement, the disturbance, coming from? Is it:

(a) from distracting noise from outside?
(b) from disturbing feelings?
(c) from following *any* line of thought?
(d) from discomfort in the body?

Taking responsibility for your resistance to letting go means becoming aware that *nothing need make you tense unless you give it that power*. A police siren or telephone ringing is merely a *fact*. Only you can turn it into a 'disturbance'. Similarly with feelings and thoughts. You won't stop feeling and thinking just because you are doing the Alpha Plan. But you will have the choice as to whether you continue to allow them to 'hook' you – or give yourself a break for a while from being pushed around by them like a Daruma doll. Remember too that you are breaking old habits: of reacting instead of non-reacting, of compulsive doing and thinking instead of watching these impulses, of preoccupation with your problems or all the things that have to be done, of being so used to holding muscles tense that letting go can feel threatening . . .

This is why we include an 'intention to relax' in the 'Essential Preparations' before starting the Alpha Plan. Either you have created an environment in which for half an hour or so it is safe for you to relax totally – or you have not. If you have decided that it is indeed safe to relax and that this is what you intend to do, then anything that tries to sabotage this is merely another form of tension to be aware of – and let go of. Any form of tension needs your cooperation to keep it in existence. Refuse to get involved in what the tension might be about, just experience whatever it is as tension *per se* with passive awareness – and use whichever technique is appropriate to maintain this passivity in the face of distractions. By and by, the Daruma doll comes to rest, the mud settles – and you come home to yourself.

PART THREE

ALPHA AT WORK

9

ALPHA FOR ENERGY, ALPHA FOR HEALTH

We have seen how important it is to learn to relax if we are to be able to survive in our stress-disease-ridden society today, let alone to enjoy any quality in life. The Alpha Plan provides a key to total relaxation at will, mental, emotional and physical, for anybody to use whenever they need to and at whatever depth they feel comfortable with or have time for. In this chapter we suggest ways in which to use 'going down to Alpha' for energy and healing.

For Unwinding after Work

1   Take a bath or a shower to refresh yourself, to start the process of becoming aware of your body again and to wash away the grime and scattered energy of the outside world.

2   Put on some music you really like, not loud and preferably slow. The best music for relaxing to in the author's experience is instrumental rather than vocal, for words are a left-hemisphere stimulator — and you have probably had enough of words all day. The more evocative of nature, space or tranquillity the better, for example, tapes of the sound of the ocean or running water, 'New Age' or Baroque music or 'music for meditation'.*

3   Make yourself *very* comfortable, put on a blindfold, and 'just listen'. You are already into Stage 1 of the Alpha Plan.

4   If you can, allow between 45 minutes and an hour really to

---

* See footnote on page 76.

enjoy your total relaxation session. You have probably had enough, too, of having to rush all day and can now take time for yourself. Making this an auto-suggestion affirmation (see page 87) might help you unwind.

5 Unless you have 'unfinished business' with the boss or a client (or any other negativity hanging over from the day's work) that needs a more specific suggestion or visualization to clear it, use either the 'beach' or 'garden' visualizations in Stage 2.

6 Remember that the goal is total letting go of tension and total passivity. If you slip into Stage 5 spontaneously *at any stage* and you feel a blissful melting of body tension happening, stay in that space and deepen it (if you wish) by relaxing into your body more. Most probably, though, after a working day, your thought process will be still very active and will need slowing down by counting the breath and use of mantra (Stage 3).

7 You may well doze off at some stage. If you do, unless you are physically exhausted, you will probably not sleep for long and will come to again feeling refreshed at a very deep level – and completely 'unwound'.

For Insomnia

The above routine, done before retiring for the night, should help people who habitually suffer from insomnia to get a good night's sleep. More tips on how to handle insomnia can be found in my book *How to Beat Fatigue* (1987).

For 'Recharging Your Batteries'

The Alpha Plan can be used for recharging your batteries during breaks between work sessions, after work when you have an evening engagement for which you want to have plenty of energy available, or any time that you are feeling drained.

1   Withdraw to the quietest place you can find and make yourself as comfortable as you can, sitting or lying.

2   Before starting Stage 1, have the intention that you will remain awake all the time, that you will allow yourself X minutes (check your watch) to relax totally, and that, by the end of that time, you will be feeling completely refreshed and full of energy.

3   Sigh deeply a few times. Close your eyes. Allow yourself to feel just how drained you are, how tight your eyes have become after having to focus so much, how much energy is buzzing around in your head after concentrating so much . . .

4   Start the Alpha Plan. Unfocus your eyes, soften them, let your contracted awareness start to expand by tuning in to the sounds reaching your ears right now . . .

5   In Stage 2 appropriate affirmations for auto-suggestion to boost your energy might be:

I am being filled with energy from the Source . . . More and more energy is flowing into me . . . more and more . . .
       or
I can feel myself relaxing . . . deeper . . . and deeper . . .

6   An effective visualization would be to imagine yourself as some sort of hollow container into which energy in the form of a fluid is being poured. See this fluid as intensely dynamic or volatile, for example like molten lava, and be totally passive as you watch and feel it filling you from your feet upwards throughout your body, warming, energizing . . . Persist with this visualization until you feel full to overflowing with energy again.

7   Allow enough time to ground yourself again after coming out of the last stage of the Alpha Plan. This is particularly necessary if you are going straight back to work, and

essential if you are working either with people or with delicate or potentially dangerous materials.

Only half an hour (or even less) of going down to Alpha will give you more zest for enjoying your evening or more renewed capacity to concentrate than if you had spent the time having a 'normal coffee break' or just 'sitting around'.

As a Daily Health Safeguard

It is understandable why 'An Alpha a Day Keeps the Doctor Away' if we think of illness not as an unfortunate accident due to chance invasion of our bodies by bacteria or viruses, but as directly related to our energy levels and the strength of our immune systems. In earlier chapters we discussed Selye's concept of energy as 'oil deposits', which, when depleted, leave us vulnerable to any bug that happens to be going around. We mentioned, too, Eastern models of 'dis-ease' as a manifestation of impoverishment or imbalance of *chi* or *prana*, and also how holistic medicine (acupuncture and homoeopathy, for example) seeks to treat not the symptoms, but the person, by stimulating and balancing the body's vital energy. We now know for sure that stress can weaken our immune system as well as being a significant factor in the genesis of heart disease, cancer and a host of other conditions, right down to the common cold.

A session of deep relaxation a day safeguards our health by:

(a) halting, at least temporarily, the drain on our energy resources of the 'fight, flight or freeze' response of the sympathetic nervous system to everyday stressors in our lives;

(b) allowing psychic and bodily energies to accumulate in this period of rest to repair the 'wear and tear' of stress and fatigue;

(c) making us aware of our 'overdoing', tension and negativity – potential health hazards if we don't know how to handle them;

(d) getting us used to slowing down and letting go of tension;
(e) making us more in touch with our needs and more sensitive
     to subtle warnings from parts of the body of any 'dis-ease'
     there – early warning, perhaps, which if heeded at this
     stage could avert the onset of more dire symptoms.

A daily session of deep and total relaxation is therefore not
only a treat, but health insurance as well. It should be seen as
prophylactic against not only stress-related illness, but *any* form
of 'unwellness'. Only by getting down to Alpha and below,
however, can relaxation go deep enough to be effective in this
way. It should be possible to set aside 30–45 minutes a day as
your time to practise 'non-doing' with the Alpha Plan. If it is
not, then you may be more busy than is good for you. But, if you
have allowed yourself to get run down to the point where your
body is forcing you into 'non-doing' by making you take to your
bed or at least take time off from work, then you can also use the
Alpha Plan to facilitate a speedier recovery and return to your
usual form.

For Self-healing

Most physicians would probably agree that, ultimately, 'all
healing is self-healing'. Their role is to facilitate the process by
which the body heals itself. Healing is more likely to happen –
and to happen faster – the more the body is allowed to rest. We
take for granted that we are ordered to bed if sick, or at least take
a day off from work to 'get over' feeling unwell. Why is this? It is
mainly to reduce demands on our energy output, to 'keep
energy in', so that it can be deployed for healing purposes where
it is most needed by the body. With their marvellous in-built
sensitivity to equilibrium, balance, stasis (define 'health' how
you will), our bodies zone in on any disturbance in any part of
their network as unerringly as spiders along their webs. But
their ability to handle intruders (i.e. pathogens), accidents and
running repairs depends on how much energy is available. The
bigger the challenge, the more energy they need to cope with it.

Whether it becomes a matter of life and death depends both on how overwhelming the challenge is and on how much vital energy we have.

So if you happen to be ill, while your doctor is trying to lessen the challenge of dis-ease to your body's defences (for example, with antibiotics), you could be assisting your body to meet that challenge by relaxing as deeply as you can to conserve and store energy. For recharging of batteries, as we have seen, the Alpha Plan is ideal and should be practised several times a day if you are ill in bed. The sleep that you will drift off into, or the resting on the borders of Alpha and Theta in Stage 5, will refresh you at a very deep level and can only help speed recovery.

Also, in this Alpha/Theta state we have a direct line to the subconscious, for we are at our most receptive. As we lie, totally passive, in the final stage of the Alpha Plan, we can both listen for messages from within as to how things are going in the battle for health, and feed in reinforcements in the form of positive energy. As well as conserving energy, use auto-suggestion and visualizations to *direct* it also to the parts of the body where it is most needed. You don't have to fight the body to do this, for it will also be naturally trying to do this itself. You may, however, have to overcome the resistance of your mind, its fear and lack of faith in the healing process. Remember the incontrovertible evidence of the power of visualizations sometimes to heal even 'incurable' disease. Experiments carried out at the George Washington Medical Centre in Washington, D C in 1984 proved that the immune system can be strengthened by practising visualization. Visualizing positively was found both to increase the number of white blood cells and also the level of thymosin-alpha-1, a hormone important to the T helper cells. This hormone produces a sense of well-being — more interesting proof that a direct physiological connection exists between putting energy into *feeling* well and actually *getting* well. It is therefore not surprising that, in England as well as in the U S A, visualization therapy is being used not only by cancer patients but also by sufferers from A I D S.

If you are well enough to read, get your family or friends who visit to bring you (as well as the flowers and the grapes, not instead of them!) books that are first-hand accounts of the seemingly miraculous power of positive thought forms to heal the body. Recommended as very readable are:

Anatomy of an Illness by Norman Cousins (Bantam, 1987)
Getting Well Again by O. Carl Simonton *et al.* (Bantam, 1986)
Love, Medicine and Miracles by Bernie S. Siegel (Rider, 1986).

When you do an affirmation or a visualization remember that whatever you give your attention to becomes more alive, because attention is energy. But make this attention-feeding to the parts of the body which are ailing effortless – don't strain or concentrate. In experiments it was found that subjects could warm their hands by giving them relaxed attention in this way – but not if they tried too hard. Here are some more reminders before we suggest possible formulas for healing affirmations and visualizations.

(a) Your subconscious is at its most receptive when you are most relaxed. The best time therefore to use auto-suggestion and visualization is in Stage 5 of the Alpha Plan when you are in 'let-go' and most in touch with your body.

(b) Try to keep your awareness as passive as possible. The calmer and more certain you are as you make affirmations or visualizations, the more deeply they will connect with where they are most needed. Defuse any tension arising from anxiety or desperation by reminding yourself that your body is healing on its own anyway – you are merely 'cheering it on'.

(c) Get the feeling into your body that what you are telling yourself or imagining is actually happening. Remind yourself that *whatever* thoughts or feelings we have will always

resonate in some way in the body, so feed into it as much
positive mental energy as you can in the form of optimism
and reassurance – and relax.

In the case of pain, after you have done everything that can be
done to attend to the cause of the pain (including seeking
professional help if necessary), there is little you *can* do except
try to persuade yourself to relax into it instead of making
yourself tenser by fighting it. In some cases (for example,
tension headaches, muscular aches) the pain may actually
disappear if you can allow yourself to stop tensing up. In every
case, alleviating panic, anxiety or depression can only make you
feel better in spite of the pain.

Healing Affirmations for Auto-suggestion

'This (symptom or pain) is my body trying to heal me.'
'I love myself totally and am allowing my body to heal itself.'
'I am relaxing into my body and allowing it to heal itself.'
'Every day, in every way, I'm getting better and better.'
'I deserve to enjoy radiant health.'
'I can feel energy filling my body . . . making it whole again.'
'By [fix a date] I shall be back to normal again.'

Visualization for Healing

People using biofeedback machines usually find that trying to
influence their body's organs and functions directly by the use
of willpower is less effective than using imagery. This makes
sense, in view of what we know about the necessity for being in
the right hemisphere of the brain rather than the left in all
dealings with the subconscious. Imagery is the pre-verbal language by means of which the Unconscious communicates its
messages to the ego, for example in dreams. In visualizations
our ego (i.e. our conscious mind) enters into a dialogue with the
Unconscious, using the same language and trying to find the

idioms, the symbols and images, which are most meaningful to it.

These will vary from person to person, in the same way as we all have different ways of expressing ourselves in everyday life. Rather than trying to impose on yourself a visualization at second hand (from a book, for example), work with the images and symbols that come into your mind spontaneously when you give passive attention in Stage 5 of the Alpha Plan to what you are experiencing in your body. (Remember, if you are a non-visual type, to substitute 'feeling' for 'seeing'.)

A visualization for healing will normally include three stages:

1   Seeing your dis-ease in some objectified way.
2   Seeing it being brought under control by the treatment you are receiving and by your own body defences.
3   Seeing yourself restored to health.

The 'action' in Stage 2 will follow on from the images that you have received in Stage 1. The Simontons reported many different ways that their patients 'saw' the battle between their white blood cells and the cancer cells: as sun melting ice, as a man trying to unjam logs, as sharks or piranhas devouring greyish cells – even as a football match! How the 'goodies' and the 'baddies' appear in your visualization is not important except in so far as you can recognize which is the 'home team' – and so long as it wins in the end. In Stage 2 a general guideline is to work to soften and harmonize, for example, harsh, disorganized, jagged images, to dispel darkness or virulent colours (common images of pain) with gold or white light, and to wash away any images of dirt, stains or garbage with crystal clear running water. In Stage 3 you picture yourself as you are when you are well, and try to get that feeling into your body. Whether or not it is God's will that you be restored completely to health, you will certainly feel more 'in charge' of your illness or your pain – and therefore more relaxed with it.

For Tuning in to Your Deeper Needs

Daily sessions of deep relaxation will not only help you to stay healthy and to cope with illness or pain. Practising the Alpha Plan regularly will also help you to stay in touch with yourself and with your emotional and spiritual needs. Normally, in Beta, we are geared to what is going on outside us, to coping with our world, our relationships, our jobs. Often we get so caught up with these exterior things, with 'getting it together' on the material plane, that we ourselves can end up feeling decidedly 'untogether': drained, unnourished and unfulfilled, without perhaps knowing why. The more we become aware of this bleak emptiness inside, the more likely we are either to try to avoid it by doing more, or to try to fill it by getting more. Running away from yourself takes a lot of energy – and sometimes money as well. The compulsive worker, eater and spender (and shop-lifter!) are on the same treadmill.

Remaining authentic and staying in touch with what we need to be happy in a world which is constantly pulling us out of ourselves by telling us both how we *should* feel and what we *should* want is not easy. But try to do it we must in some way or another, not only if we are to experience satisfaction and quality in our lives, but also to stay healthy mentally and emotionally, to feel real. If our lives are not to be lived at a very superficial level, if we are to continue growing psychologically and spiri-tually, if we are not to risk sterility or breakdown, each of us needs to be engaged in dialogue with the deeper levels of our being. Jung saw the psyche as self-regulating. Striving always after wholeness, it seeks constantly to compensate for one-sided living, to urge us on to become who we really are. The Uncon-scious speaks to us in our quiet moments, warning of false directions, guiding us back to balance and onwards to whole-ness – or 'wellness', the same thing. If we do not heed its messages our dreams can become nightmares and our lives neurotic. But if we can get into the habit of listening to and trusting our intuition, it develops. We become 'tuned in' to our own process to the point where we sense straight away which things are right for us and which are harmful.

How we prefer to stay in touch with the deeper levels of our being is very personal. Some of us meditate, some pray, some are in analysis. Others will find it in nature, in music, in a special relationship perhaps, or simply in taking time to sit and reflect. What facilitates contact with our inner selves in each case, however, is switching off the noisy world and the mind for a while and relaxing into present-centred awareness and feeling. A daily session of 'going down to Alpha' is a convenient way of structuring such a 'meditative space' into your busy day during which you can feel who you are again – and what you are becoming.

10

STAYING RELAXED

In this chapter we consider ways in which the Alpha Plan can be adapted for handling tension in everyday life situations when it would not be possible or appropriate to lie down and go through all the stages. How to adapt the Plan to stay relaxed in the course of our working day will be clearer if we remind ourselves of what we have learned about the dynamics of tension and relaxation, and the pathways out of Beta down into Alpha.

In the questionnaires at the beginning of Chapter 3 you were asked to list your favourite ways of relaxing after work and why you thought they did, in fact, relax you. If we now reconsider our favourite ways to relax in the light of the five pathways to Alpha that we have incorporated in the Alpha Plan, *how* they work to relax us perhaps becomes more obvious. Here are some examples of how you may have been 'getting down to Alpha' so far, without, perhaps, knowing you were doing so.

1. 'SENSES RELAXED' as a result of

~ entertainment, for example watching T V shows, theatre, cinema, ballet, some spectator sports
~ getting absorbed browsing in a museum, art gallery or street market
~ 'window-shopping'
~ curling up with a good book
~ listening to music
~ taking a nap

2. 'FEELINGS POSITIVE' as a result of

~ going on holiday
~ being in 'good company'
~ getting absorbed in hobbies
~ playing with the kids

3. 'MIND SLOWING DOWN' as a result of

~ meditating
~ practising yoga
~ contemplative prayer
~ practising martial arts
~ communing with nature

4. 'BODY RELAXING' as a result of

~ bathing
~ exercising
~ participating in sports
~ being massaged
~ dancing

5. 'LETTING GO' as a result of

~ drinking alcohol
~ celebrating
~ love-making
~ catharsis (for example in therapy, or at high-energy events like pop concerts or football matches)

Obviously there is overlap, since our senses, emotions, minds and bodies are not really separate at all. 'Communing with nature', for example by going fishing, climbing, enjoying a beautiful view, or taking a long walk in the countryside or along the seashore, will relax us at more than one level of the model we have been using. The enormous popularity of jogging (with or without a Walkman) may be that it kills so many birds with one stone: sense relaxation, slowed-down mind, body awareness. Our annual holiday, for most of us the major relaxation event of the year, ideally relaxes us at all levels. (Unless, of course, air traffic control or the baggage handlers are on strike, our hotel has overbooked and we get 'Mediterranean tummy'.) This is when, if all goes well, we 'get away from it all' – from the sensory overload of the city, from our worries and problems, from our jobs – and give ourselves time and space to pamper our bodies, to have fun with like-minded companions and 'let our hair down' a bit.

But sometimes things do not always go so well. Sometimes we may not have time for a morning jog, may be too tired after work, or may have too much on our minds to enjoy it anyway when we do make it out to the park. As we have suggested elsewhere, 'socializing' is not always as relaxing as convention and good manners would have us pretend. We may come back from that party we had been looking forward to, drained from small talk and overloaded with liquor, wondering why on earth we ever went in the first place. Sometimes we may find ourselves too restless to sit and meditate, or end up merely jaded rather than relaxed after an evening spent watching too much television because we wouldn't have known what to do if we had switched it off. And even if our holiday did come up to expectations and we had a whale of a time, after we have been back in town for a few days that 'holiday feeling' (i.e. the Alpha state) starts vanishing just as surely (and usually as fast) as our suntan. Our ability to relax will remain a hit-and-miss affair, unless we become as conscious of what works to dispel tension and what doesn't as most of us nowadays have become about what we should include in or omit from our daily diet in order to stay healthy.

Here is a check-list for reference, to remind you of what makes us feel more tense or more relaxed.

1 TENSION	2 RELAXATION
over-involvement in 'the outer'	detachment
time urgency	unstructured time
overdoing	passivity
focused attention	unfocused awareness
noisy environment	quiet environment
discomfort	comfort

unresolved negative feelings
  (e.g. anxiety, anger, jealousy)
	positive or neutral mood
	  (e.g. non-serious)

overactive mind	not thinking much
worrying	positive thinking
shallow breathing	slow, deep breathing
tensed muscles	relaxed muscles
low body awareness	centred in the body

The Alpha Plan as described so far (i.e. Stages 1 to 5 done consecutively in peace and quiet at home) takes us from the top of column 1 above ('over-involvement with the outer', i.e. Beta) down to the bottom of column 2 ('centred in the body', i.e. the relaxed Alpha state). We envisaged this not as a direct linear descent, but as a spiral staircase with five 'landings' on which we pause in turn to relax our tension at each stage, and to any of which we may have to bring the light of our awareness back if tension re-establishes itself there. We can obviously only 'go down to Alpha' fully with the Alpha Plan in this way when we have the time and the space. We have recommended that this time and space be created at least once a day, preferably after finishing work to allow ourselves to recover from the day's stress and recharge batteries for the evening's enjoyment. But what can we do to stay relaxed (or at least to handle our tension) while we are actually 'out there' in the busy world? How can we adapt the Alpha Plan to help us when we start feeling tense, for example at work or on social occasions?

We have seen above that the reasons you manage to relax in 'off-duty' hours while 'doing your thing' are the same reasons you relax when doing the Alpha Plan. The difference is that with the Alpha Plan you have the intention of making dimly-felt tension conscious, and then you use specific and well-tried awareness techniques to dissolve it progressively. Even though we may not be able to follow the Alpha Plan when we are 'out in the world' in the same way as we can do at home, we can still draw on its principles and apply its techniques whenever we feel things are 'getting on top of us' in the course of the day.

Here are a few suggestions of things you can do whenever you start to get drained, tense or stressed. Not only will you feel better, more relaxed and centred, but taking the effort out of the job or the uptightness out of the situation will make for more efficiency. It should be possible to do some at least of the following, however busy you are or however formal the occasion.

~   If possible, take a break, however short.
~   Make yourself more comfortable, any way you can.
~   If you can, withdraw to somewhere quieter.
~   If you can, be alone for a while.
~   If you can, close your eyes, listen to sounds, count your breaths with mantra, tune into any body sensations.
~   Cut out unnecessary talking and movement.
~   If you have to talk, break eye contact, soften your voice, 'lighten it up', for example with humour.
~   Become an observer rather than an active participator for a while.
~   Do less, listen more.
~   Unfocus your eyes (don't squint – just relax them).
~   Rest your eyes on the most pleasant things (or people) in your surroundings.
~   Tune into what you are feeling.
~   Enjoy a daydream of where you would most like to be right now.
~   Repeat inwardly a calming affirmation (e.g. 'RELAX-(ING)'.

~ See the positive aspects of what is happening.

~ Say something positive or humorous to somebody.

~ Soften your expression.

~ Choose to be gentler, kinder to those around you.

~ Try to see the other person's point of view.

~ Tune in to what the other person is really feeling.

~ Share how you really feel rather than blame, criticize or defend.

~ Risk asking for what you need.

~ Choose to accept whatever is happening.

~ Choose to forgive whoever or whatever has disturbed you.

~ Choose to surrender to the other person on this occasion.

~ Choose to accept yourself exactly as you are.

~ Become aware of your breathing and combine it with a mantra.

~ If disturbed, breathe more deeply and slowly – and count 1 to 10.

~ Become aware of paranoid thoughts – and stop scaring yourself.

~ Use affirmations to counteract anxiety, panic, ebbing confidence, etc.

~ Become more aware of your body.

~ Open out your posture (e.g. uncross legs, unfold arms).

~ If possible, stand up and stretch.

~ Bring more awareness and energy to your body any way that is appropriate (e.g. massaging neck, face, hands).

~ Ground yourself by feeling your feet on the floor and wiggling your toes.

~ Treat yourself to something.

~ Relax and enjoy.

Remember our model of the spiral staircase leading down from Beta to Alpha? On which 'landing' is your tension manifesting? *How* exactly do you feel tense right now? If you are not sure, work your way down the 'staircase' by asking yourself the following questions:

~ What am I aware of in my environment? (i.e. Senses
  Relaxed?)
~ What feelings am I in touch with right now? (i.e. Feelings
  Positive?)
~ What am I telling myself in my head? (i.e. Mind Slowing
  Down?)
~ What am I aware of in my body? (i.e. Body Relaxing?)
~ What am I unwilling to let go of? (i.e. Letting Go?).

At whichever level (or levels) tension is mainly being experienced, *contraction* of some kind will be present. It is useful, when you want to relax, to remember that tension and *contraction* go together, as do relaxation and *expansion*. Think of the expressions we use to convey the idea of tension and negativity, or of a relaxed, positive state.

Here are a few:

CONTRACTION	EXPANSION
'that shrinking feeling'	'an expansive mood'
'X made me feel small'	'walking tall'
'wound up', 'uptight'	'unwind', 'loosen up'
'a closed person (mind)'	'an open person', 'keep an open mind'
'narrow-minded'	'broad-minded'
'tight-lipped'	
'under pressure'	'the pressure's off'
'feeling hemmed in'	'having space to breathe'

As well as *feeling* contracted when tense, contraction is actually *happening* to us. Awareness of our surroundings is narrowed by intense concentration, even more so by eyes strained by looking too much. We can become preoccupied with a problem or obsessed by jealousy, for example, to the exclusion of all else. In confrontation we are often so defensive about our own point of view or wanting to be right at all costs that we may not even hear what the other person is saying. The most obvious signs of contraction, though, are shown in the body, which truly does seem to 'shrink' with muscle tension. The face tightens, shoulders hunch, we tend to adopt locked-in, tight postures.

Whenever, therefore, you feel tense, try to become aware of *how* you are experiencing contraction – and do the opposite as far as is possible in the circumstances. Open out your body posture and 'take your space'; give yourself 'breathing space' when you are under pressure. Allow yourself (and others) the space to be who you are and feel what you are feeling and, possibly, to choose to share it. Stop concentrating for a while, 'lose your mind and come to your senses'. Let go of anything that is disturbing you by withdrawing attention from it, by 'expanding to include' rather than resisting or polarizing against it. Remember that, in the same way that you gave power to whatever is causing your tension to make you tighten up, so you have the power to relax that tension. *Your power to relax your tension is your attention.* Whatever you give active attention to, you get more of. The more you concentrate on something, the more you will experience it. The techniques for relaxation used in the Alpha Plan are all to do with attention – about withdrawing it from what keeps us in Beta and feeding it to what will take us down to Alpha. From his experience of biofeedback with the 'Mind Mirror' Geoffrey G. Blundell tells us: 'Beta is the usual waking rhythm of the brain associated with active thinking, active attention, focus on the outside world or solving concrete problems.' A predominance of Alpha brainwaves, associated with inward directed attention, relaxed awareness and feelings of well-being, 'is reduced or eliminated by opening the eyes, by hearing unfamiliar sounds, by anxiety or by mental concentration.' (*The Meaning of EEG*, Audio Ltd, London)

11

ALPHA FOR EVERYBODY

In Chapter 1 we met Mike, Alan, Kate, Margaret and Jim. Let us now see how they could apply the Alpha Plan in their everyday lives to find relief from the particular tensions that arise in the course of a normal day. As we do so, you may see more clearly how exactly you too may be contracting yourself in the course of your day and how you could use the 'Alpha approach', not only to repair the ravages of stress, but to handle stress as it arises – or even to forestall it.

Mike

Mike's main problem is that during his working day he is relentlessly 'on the go'. He has no *space*, psychological or physical, and allows himself to get drained by his own perfectionism. The latter is a pressure he puts on himself because of his pride in doing a good job, his need for approval from the people he is giving a service to, and his anxiety about ensuring (through good reports) future work. He is aware that, like actors, he is as good as his last job.

Having to be 'out' so much means that Mike's level of Beta will be high (which is why he may experience panic if things go wrong), and he will be prone to tension at all levels.

Sensory Overload

From being surrounded by people, noise, traffic; the unceasing demands on his attention and energy; having to *look* so much; having to maintain eye contact with and being scrutinized (often critically) by perhaps 30 or 40 people when he is addressing the group as a whole; having always to be in control.

Emotional Tension

From being unable to express any personal feelings (for example impatience or irritation) which might be unprofessional or occasion a complaint to his employer; having to *please* all the time; feeling responsible for anything going wrong.

Mental Tension

From having to concentrate continuously; having to remember so much and communicate it in an interesting form; having to talk so much; working always against time.

Bodily Stress

From having to sit or stand for long periods; having to generate energy with often unresponsive people; having to project his voice to be heard by the one who always stands at the back of the group cupping his ear.

WHAT MIKE CAN DO

(and anyone else in his kind of job involving public speaking, serving customers, working under pressure, for example lecturers and demonstrators, shop assistants, catering staff, airline cabin crews, etc.)

(a) While Working

1 'SENSES RELAXED'

Switch off whenever he has the opportunity, even for very short periods, by

~ unfocusing his eyes except when he absolutely needs to see something;

~ appearing to make eye contact with members of the group while lecturing to them but in fact 'keeping his energy in' by letting his softened gaze rove around the group, in between them, looking past or slightly over their heads. By unfocusing and not getting 'sucked in' to the very mixed bag of energy being projected at him from the eyes of his audience (whether curious, critical, placating, lustful or hostile), Mike will feel less uncomfortable at being scrutinized, and save his energy;

~ taking refreshments, chatting with his driver (but not if the latter is in a negative mood);

~ remaining silent when appropriate, for example when the group are all so busy taking photographs they wouldn't be listening anyway;

~ withdrawing into his own space when the group are happily occupied, for example in bookshops, souvenir shops.

2   'FEELINGS POSITIVE'

Work at being more at ease while giving his services by

~ bringing a positive attitude, for example having the intention to enjoy the day's work rather than resenting being there;

~ setting boundaries: being helpful and pleasant while at the same time maintaining a professional distance;

~ being less serious: lightening up his interactions with humour;

~ validating his own knowledge, professionalism, expertise to himself with an affirmation, for example, 'I really am doing a good job here';

~ visualizing his own role in a less anxiety-generating way, for example imagining that the group are friends visiting London and he is enjoying showing them his home town;

~ being clear about the limits of his responsibility when things go wrong and there are complaints: not tolerating personal abuse or invalidation but 'hearing' the client's problem;
~ giving more attention to the well-disposed and the bare minimum to the scowlers and attention-getters;
~ if exposed to negativity, warding it off by visualizing himself protected by a circle of golden light.

3   'MIND SLOWING DOWN'

Becoming aware of just how fast he is thinking and talking – and whether in fact this rate of energy expenditure is either necessary or desirable; saving energy by

~ slowing down the pace at which he works;
~ omitting inessential detail;
~ when not talking, breathing slow and deep;
~ breathing into the *hara*;
~ repeating inwardly a relaxing mantra, e.g. 'RELAX-(ING)';
~ answering questions simply and in just enough detail – without anxiously 'over-feeding' with unsolicited information or feeling responsible for the other person 'getting' it. (Questions are often 'hooks' to get attention: the other person is often not really as interested in the answer as in being noticed or in control.)

4   'BODY RELAXING'

Trying to stay centred and grounded with so much happening so quickly by

~ maintaining an open body posture;
~ speaking from the *hara*;
~ feeling feet on the floor;
~ becoming aware of any tension in the body (for example, hunched shoulders, tight jaw/belly) – and relaxing it.

5 'LETTING GO'

Of attachment to being perfect; of being liked by everybody all the time; of worrying about whether or not customers are satisfied rather than about offering the best service possible in the circumstances (i.e. taking responsibility for whether they 'take in' what he is offering them or not, rather than for just 'delivering the goods'. Whether they enjoy it or not is up to them – and there are some customers who cannot allow themselves to appreciate or enjoy *anything*).

(b) After Work

~ *Shower or hot bath* to wash away the day's grime and scattered energy and to start the process of 'relaxing into the body'.

~ *Put on soft music* to start the 'unwinding' process and the shift from the left to the right hemisphere of the brain. The best tapes to play are those that are calming and evocative of nature and space.*

~ *Dim lights/lie down/put on a blindfold.*

~ *Alpha Plan for at least 30–45 minutes.*

People like Mike who have been 'on the go' all day, assailed from all sides and without a moment to themselves, specially need to counterbalance the contraction that follows naturally from such overexposure to the outside world and output of energy by:

~ being alone, quiet and passive for as long as is possible to allow batteries to recharge;

~ coming back to a sense of having space for themselves, freed from having to meet others' demands, by visualizations, for example of deserted beaches, wide-open spaces, of enjoying wealth and leisure, of favourite holiday haunts; by

* See footnote on page 76.

fantasies that restore a sense of autonomy, potency, or (if it's been a particularly trying day), rebellion;

~ spending more time on slowing down the thinking process (which, typically, in high Beta states that go with over-active involvement in the outside world, will still be churning on) by counting the breath and repeating a mantra;

~ progressive body relaxation with particular attention to relaxing the muscles of the face (the professional 'persona' or public mask), tongue, lips, jaw and throat (these will still want to go on working);

~ letting go of *everything* – including the things that one *could* have said to that difficult customer . . .

Alan

Alan needs to come back into the present out of the past, out of the left hemisphere of the brain (concerned with words, logic, ideas), if he is to experience relief from the contraction arising from too much concentration. This means that, when he takes a break from studying, he needs to 'come to his senses' and ground himself in his body and in contact with his surroundings. He needs also to be aware of his anxiety about success or failure in getting his degree, and the stress this adds to the pressure he is already under to get all his revision done in time.

WHAT ALAN CAN DO

(and anyone whose job entails long periods of concentrated attention, e.g. students, academics, architects, typists, research workers – and, of course, writers!)

1 'SENSES RELAXED'

Minimize tension while engaged in close work by ensuring

~ adequate lighting on the object of concentration;

~ maximum comfort;
~ minimum disturbance;
~ resting of eyes every so often (and returning awareness to the present) by raising them from concentrating and letting them rest, unfocused, on some pleasing object(s) in the room, for example plants, flowers, paintings;
~ checking and adjusting of body posture for more comfort, specially neck, back and shoulders.

Take breaks at intervals every 1½–2 hours for refreshment by

~ taking a short walk to get some fresh air or a change of scene;
~ having a small treat;
~ deep, slow breathing before an open window;
~ lying down, blindfolded, listening to music or sounds from outside.

2 'FEELINGS POSITIVE'

~ cancelling out any dismay, whenever he finds himself telling himself he is going to fail or that it is all too much, by making positive affirmations about his performance and prospects;
~ visualizing total success and how that feels – in Alan's case, imagining himself accepting his degree at the graduation ceremony, seeing his name on the scroll and being congratulated by parents and fellow students – getting this feeling of pride and relief into his body; visualizing the rewards of his efforts.

3 'MIND SLOWING DOWN'

~ closing eyes, counting breaths + mantra;
~ allowing distraction from concentration for a while when getting mentally overloaded by doing something mindless (i.e. not involving concentration – and preferably not read-

ing), for example, looking out of the window, daydreaming, listening to music, watering the house plants, playing with the cat (or, if there is no cat available, just enjoying a gossip with whoever does happen to be around!).

4 'BODY RELAXING'

~ periodically standing up, stretching and flexing muscles to counteract contraction due to 'holding';

~ exercise of any kind that will bring back body awareness, and especially if combined with fresh air at the same time, for example a walk or jog in the park (if a 'nine to fiver', during the lunch break?).

5 'LETTING GO'

~ being clear that, after work has been put away, 'that is it' until the next morning;

~ letting go of anxiety: being sincere in his approach but not serious;

~ having fun with friends;

~ dancing (particularly good for shaking off care and tension).

Before going to bed

~ *'Mindless entertainment'* to start the 'winding down' process. The less reading or intellectual involvement the better.

~ *Shower or hot bath.* Wash hair, imagining the water is washing away all the thoughts still buzzing round, leaving the head clear . . .

~ *Full Alpha Plan in bed before drifting off into sleep.*

'Intellectual' workers like Alan need especially to counter-balance contraction and 'recharge their batteries' by

~ formulating the intention to have a good night's sleep;

~   self-validation of their progress, prospects and ability to
    recall facts when needed (for example in examinations);
~   visualization of successful completion of the project;
~   awareness of breathing + relaxing mantra;
~   progressive body relaxation and visualization of being filled
    with energy and confidence.

Kate

Kate's situation will be a familiar one, not only to those readers
who are employed in one of the 'helping professions' (doctors,
nurses, social workers, counsellors, teachers, etc.), but also to
parents, and to those looking after the elderly at home. However professional and/or caring one tries to be, inevitably there
are times when one feels one has just had enough of giving
attention to other people – and still the job has to be done.
Rather than acting out this more or less conscious resentment
(or 'acting in' by feeling guilty), it is more productive to see such
contraction as a natural correction of over-extending oneself in
caring for others for too long without also giving attention to
one's own needs – and to take responsibility for getting these
met. Readers who recognize this as a problem in their own lives
will find more ideas on how to handle it in my *Take Charge of
Your Life (How Not to Be a Victim)* (1988).

Kate needs to resolve her confusion about responsibility,
giving and being given to, 'feeding' and 'being fed'. She is
allowing herself to get drained by the demands upon her, and
her negativity is the part of her that needs to be given to
for a change sulking, or saying 'Enough!' She needs to set
boundaries to her giving and availability, to ask for support from
her family and to give to herself more. She could start by
considering whether she needs to cut down on her case-load
and/or take a holiday. Meanwhile, during the intervals between
counselling sessions, she could nourish herself in the following
ways.

1 'SENSES RELAXED'

~ Keep the sign 'COUNSELLING IN PROGRESS – DO NOT DIS-
TURB' on the door to ensure privacy, make herself comfort-
able on the couch (or in the armchair) and 'go down to
Alpha', even for just a few minutes.

~ Treat herself to refreshment or 'goodies' she has brought in
to work with her.

~ Leave the building for a short walk or to sit in the garden if
it's a fine day.

~ Chat, read a newspaper (or do the crossword) in the staff
counsellors' room.

2 'FEELINGS POSITIVE'

~ Clear any disturbing counter-transference she has had from
the last counselling session, if necessary by discussing it
with colleagues or her supervisor. (Expressing her *own*
feelings will counterbalance having to be a supportive and
attentive listener in her work.)

~ Close her eyes and tune into what she really needs most in
her life right now – and visualize herself receiving it.

~ Reflect on how exactly she gives more than she should (and
perhaps needs to) to everybody except herself and tune into
what need this fills in herself or what it says about her own
lack of self-esteem.

~ Visualize herself as one of her own clients: what is her real
problem and what does she need to do for herself?

~ Take responsibility for setting boundaries, getting more
space, and asking for more support from her family.

~ Make affirmations to open herself to receiving and being
more loving to herself as well as to the people she cares for,
e.g. *'It's O K to ask for what I need too.' 'I can allow myself to
receive / to be vulnerable also'* will counteract guilt or fear at
not being 'strong', her use of 'giving' to stay in control.

NOTE: With her awareness and experience as a professionally

trained counsellor Kate will, if she gives herself time and reflects, come up with the right answers for her. By this process of introspection she will also be moving out of Beta's preoccupation with the external, and giving herself some nourishment in the form of attention to her own process.

3 'MIND SLOWING DOWN'

Working as she does so much with her intuition, listening and giving free attention (i.e. passive awareness) and therefore much of the time using the right hemisphere of the brain, an overactive mind for Kate should not be a special stressor of her profession (as is becoming *emotionally* drained by clients).

4 'BODY RELAXING'

Kate's special need is for self-nourishment and for recharging her emotional batteries. The attention her body needs from her is therefore not so much relaxation of muscular tension but *pampering*.

After work Kate could:

~　Treat herself to something she will probably feel guilty about as being somewhat extravagant and faintly decadent – but will feel great after – for example a sauna, a solarium session, a massage, some aromatherapy or other similarly sensually satisfying 'whole body' experience. (Or she could go to the hairdresser or shopping for a new outfit – anything will do that feels like a treat. If it involves other people giving her body caring energy in some form, for example, massage, so much the better.)

~　Allow her family to feed her once in a while – either by preparing the evening meal or taking her out to dinner to show their appreciation.

~　Nourish herself by luxuriating in a fragrant hot bath before retiring to the bedroom to spend as long as she wants with herself and the Alpha Plan, having first put one of the day's affirmations into effect by risking asking not to be disturbed for half an hour or so. (Kate is not used to either taking space for herself or asking for things, so of course she will not be over-generous with herself until she realizes that her family can indeed look after themselves quite happily even though she absents herself for a while.)

~ Alpha Plan for as long as she can tolerate totally relaxing. Professional 'feeders' of others like Kate may need to use auto-suggestion to counteract their resistance to letting go of their concern for others temporarily, and their fear of being 'selfish' or of feeling vaguely threatened by losing control if they relax and let the world get along without them. Suitable affirmations for this purpose might be '*I allow myself to be given to more and more*' or '*If I take for myself, I have something to give.*' Kate can counteract any residual self-pity at feeling neglected by reminding herself of all the things she has already been given and takes for granted, for example '*I am grateful for my husband, my children, my home . . .*'

Total let-go might be threatening to a 'controller' like Kate unless combined with a reassuring visualization that she is being 'held', i.e. supported in some way, that it is safe to let go without 'being dropped', falling . . .

Margaret

If Margaret is to enjoy any quality in her life she has to move from the position of being a victim – of her arthritis, of her pessimism, of her anxiety – and must learn to trust her doctor, her own capacity for self-help and, ultimately, life. Margaret's situation is that of many people today who are invalids or ailing, elderly and perhaps widowed or living alone, or are simply passing through a difficult period in their lives and under more or less acute stress, for example bereavement, divorce, financial crisis, emotional distress, illness or pain.

NOTE: It is assumed that, where necessary, professional advice or treatment has already been sought, for example medical or legal help, and counselling; and that anything that can be done (such as use of medication) to help the situation has been or is already being done.

The higher the Beta level the more the panic, desperation or restlessness. Counteract this by 'going down to Alpha': lie down and do the full Alpha Plan (if this is possible) or at least lower the Beta level by applying the Plan as below.

1   'SENSES RELAXED'

Counteract jangled nerves and 'end of tether' desperation by:

~   resting quietly, eyes closed, listening to soothing music (for example 'meditation tapes') or to sounds from the environment; O R
~   keeping energy 'in' by cutting out unnecessary output through restlessness and 'softening' it with gentler gaze, expression, tone of voice and movements;
~   distraction from obsession with emotional or physical discomfort in any way that is enjoyable, for example radio, T V, 'treats', good company.

2   'FEELINGS POSITIVE'

~   Counteract contraction from anxiety, depression, catastrophic expectations by becoming aware of what these are (i.e. not *denying* them) and then affirming or visualizing the opposite. Examples of positive affirmations and healing visualizations and how to make them are given on page 104.

Margaret, for example, could use a visualization suggested by Dr Simonton (in *Getting Well Again*, p. 148) of picturing her arthritic joints pitted, irritated, with little granules on the surfaces which are being picked up by her white blood cells. Visualizations should always end with things transformed for the better. Margaret's would end with her visualizing her joint surfaces smooth and herself active again, free from pain.

~ Share feelings with a person (trained counsellor or not) who above all is able to *listen* with full attention, and get some relief at least from knowing that one's pain has been *heard*.

~ Try, hard though it undoubtedly is (and, for those who have just about had as much as they can take of suffering, perhaps a counsel of perfection), to respond to pain with acceptance and positive feelings (for example, for those poor, suffering joints) rather than with resistance or negativity (for example, cursing them), which always seems to make things worse. When everything around is turning into a nightmare, put out more love – including loving yourself for not feeling loving. After all, what is there to lose?

3 'MIND SLOWING DOWN'

~ distraction from obsession with 'the problem' by keeping occupied in enjoyable or at least non-stressful ways; O R
~ counting the breaths;
~ mantra, for example, '*This too shall pass*';
~ centring awareness in the heart; O R
~ praying for comfort, healing and the grace of acceptance.

4 'BODY RELAXING'

Practise progressive body relaxation, starting with the feet, in spite of the clamour from where you are hurting. Do not tighten up by resisting pain. Rather try to allow it to be there and relax into it. A useful device to facilitate this is to breathe into the pain. Imagine as you do so that with each inhalation you are directing soothing and healing energy to the suffering part of you. As you exhale, imagine that the outgoing breath is taking with it congestion, inflammation, toxins . . . This is a good time to practise other healing visualization and auto-suggestion also, when you are as relaxed as you probably can be. Try to *see* the pain. What colour is it? What shape is it? What area does it cover? Is it moving or stationary? Does it change in any way as you observe it? Tune into it. Why is it there? What is its message to you? If it had a voice, what would it be saying about how you could feel better?

5 'LETTING GO'

~ of resistance to experiencing physical pain or other suffering. By allowing yourself to experience fully what is your
   reality right now, you take away much of its power to hurt
   and make you contract;
~ of anxiety. In spite of what your mind has been telling you,
   choose to trust that all is happening as it should be. Faith
   does not need proof – it is a non-logical choice. Take a jump.
   Who's to say you are wrong?

Jim

There is not much we can do about Jim. The others want to relax – he doesn't. He has too much invested in being successful, in control, high-powered, outwardly orientated – and therefore addicted to being in Beta. There are many things he needs to do to meet the risks of being a 'Type A'. He should of course allow himself to convalesce, perhaps by taking his wife off on a long cruise (which he can certainly afford). He needs to delegate responsibility, to slow down, to make changes in his attitude to work and his life-style . . . But he won't – even though he has had clear warnings of what might happen if he doesn't. But

before we are too harsh on Jim, let us look into this phenomenon, so true of many people today, of not being able to 'switch
off' even though they know they risk killing themselves if they
don't.

It is not always that we don't know how to switch off. Many
people (and that includes the author) will take the trouble to
learn relaxation techniques, for example, yoga, meditation, tai
chi, autogenics – and then 'forget' to use them when the going
gets rough. Such forgetting is, as Freud pointed out, a sign of
resistance. But why should one have resistance to something so
pleasurable as relaxing?

Resistance to Relaxing

'Forgetting' your daily deep relaxation session, restlessness and
difficulty in letting go in the Alpha Plan could be due to a
number of things.

1   Addiction to Excitement

Remember that one can become addicted to virtually anything
– including living at a fast pace, or working flat out under
pressure. Some people enjoy 'being speedy' for the sake of it,
whether through taking drugs or driving fast cars, others 'get a
buzz' from being busy bees, whether professionally or socially –
it is the same thing. The fact that many people enjoy scaring
themselves has proved a rich mine to the film industry (witness
the extraordinary success of *Jaws*, for example). The line between experiencing high Beta states as panic or as thrilling is
thin: sports and hobbies that 'turn on' some *aficionados* would
traumatize others (sky-diving, for example).

*'Going down to Alpha' is to withdraw from outside stimulation for a
while.*

2   Avoidance of Boredom

Boredom is one of the things we try to avoid most in our society. One of the most wounding things one can say about anything or anyone is simply '*He (She, It) is boring*', or, even worse, '*You are a bore.*' 'Boredom' would probably be defined generally as 'nothing happening'. Since we are terrified either of being bored or of being thought to be boring, we are uncomfortable when there is 'nothing happening' – which is why we try to 'find things to do', 'make conversation', 'fill time', etc.

   'Sitting quietly, doing nothing' can feel boring.

3   Fear of Emptiness

The sometimes almost palpable uneasiness that permeates a room when people who do not know each other well have run out of small talk is a manifestation of this fear of 'nothing happening'. The more fearful we are of emptiness (and what might come out of it), the more we tend to structure our future to protect ourselves against any nasty surprises. 'Our future' includes everything from the next moment, to next week, to the rest of our lives. So, to feel safe, we break silences, fill our diaries with engagements, take out insurance. We want to know what's coming next.

   Any meditative technique (including the Alpha Plan) is aimed at 'staying with' what remains when we let go of our 'props'.

4   Fear of Aloneness

Those evenings when we stay home on our own, especially when there is 'nothing on telly' and nothing needs doing around the house, can be torture for many people who confuse aloneness with loneliness. They may experience discomfort ranging from mild depression to panic if there is nobody else around and the phone doesn't ring.

   'Going down to Alpha' is about ENJOYING being alone with yourself.

5   Social Conditioning

Extroversion is more highly valued in our Western societies than introversion. To call somebody 'introverted' or 'self-centred' is somewhat derogatory, implying narcissism, selfishness, lack of social skills, egocentricity and the like. Someone who is 'too withdrawn' could be schizoid, and if he is 'too introspective' he may need 'bringing out of himself'. Social success and professional advancement come more easily to those who are 'outgoing', 'good mixers', 'dynamic' and 'ambitious', so it is hardly surprising that many feel they have to 'stay up' in Beta for survival, let alone to maintain their standard of living.

The pathways to Alpha involve focusing on the inner, dropping the outer reality.

6   Fear of Letting Go

The more we look 'out', the less we are in touch with our own process, the more it, i.e. we ourselves, becomes an unknown quantity. Since, as we have seen, we are afraid of the Unknown, we may resist relaxing too deeply for fear of what may surface if we let go.

Letting go involves trusting our own process and intuition for guidance and balance.

7   Identification with Thinking and Doing

Our education and training has been overloaded on left hemisphere brain functions so that we feel more comfortable with logic, ideas, words and activity than with feelings, experiencing and 'just being'.

Relaxing deeply involves temporarily withdrawing energy from being either a 'thinker' or a 'doer' – which may feel like 'losing yourself' or 'not being real'.

Old habits die hard. So expect yourself at first to want to turn the Alpha Plan into yet another chore to be 'done', and to find that you are judging yourself for whether you 'did it right' and 'made yourself relax'. Expect your mind to fight hard against being 'switched off' — it is not used to *you* telling *it* how to behave. Don't be too ambitious: remember we are not aiming at 'no-thoughts-at-all' (the zen 'no-mind') but at 'taking no notice' of the thoughts that are there, *whatever they are*. Persist in giving passive attention to your present awareness, to feeling good, to your breathing and to what you are experiencing in your body. Remain indifferent to the efforts of the chattering monkey inside your head to lure you away from your intention of relaxing totally by dragging you back into the tangled Beta jungle of thinking, worrying, problem-solving and future-tripping. Risk — and trust — that the world keeps on turning even though you let go of it, and that letting go of *that* problem for a while does not mean that it is never ever going to be solved. (On the contrary, the solution may well be more obvious after resting in Alpha for a while — certainly it was for Einstein.) There is a time to think and to act — and a time to allow yourself just to 'be'. The time you set aside for 'going down to Alpha' may be the only time in a busy day when you can allow yourself this luxury of 'just being'. Look on the Alpha Plan, therefore, not as something you 'do' (or, worse, 'have' to do), but as something to 'play' with, a treat, a daily holiday you give yourself. *Enjoy it.*

INDEX

FOR THE BEST IN PAPERBACKS, LOOK FOR THE 🐧

In every corner of the world, on every subject under the sun, Penguin represents quality and variety – the very best in publishing today.

For complete information about books available from Penguin – including Pelicans, Puffins, Peregrines and Penguin Classics – and how to order them, write to us at the appropriate address below. Please note that for copyright reasons the selection of books varies from country to country.

In the United Kingdom: Please write to *Dept E.P., Penguin Books Ltd, Harmondsworth, Middlesex, UB7 0DA*

If you have any difficulty in obtaining a title, please send your order with the correct money, plus ten per cent for postage and packaging, to *PO Box No 11, West Drayton, Middlesex*

In the United States: Please write to *Dept BA, Penguin, 299 Murray Hill Parkway, East Rutherford, New Jersey 07073*

In Canada: Please write to *Penguin Books Canada Ltd, 2801 John Street, Markham, Ontario L3R 1B4*

In Australia: Please write to the *Marketing Department, Penguin Books Australia Ltd, P.O. Box 257, Ringwood, Victoria 3134*

In New Zealand: Please write to the *Marketing Department, Penguin Books (NZ) Ltd, Private Bag, Takapuna, Auckland 9*

In India: Please write to *Penguin Overseas Ltd, 706 Eros Apartments, 56 Nehru Place, New Delhi, 110019*

In Holland: Please write to *Penguin Books Nederland B.V., Postbus 195, NL–1380AD Weesp, Netherlands*

In Germany: Please write to *Penguin Books Ltd, Friedrichstrasse 10–12, D–6000 Frankfurt Main 1, Federal Republic of Germany*

In Spain: Please write to *Longman Penguin España, Calle San Nicolas 15, E–28013 Madrid, Spain*

In France: Please write to *Penguin Books Ltd, 39 Rue de Montmorency, F-75003, Paris, France*

In Japan: Please write to *Longman Penguin Japan Co Ltd, Yamaguchi Building, 2–12–9 Kanda Jimbocho, Chiyoda-Ku, Tokyo 101, Japan*

PENGUIN HEALTH

The Prime of Your Life   Dr Miriam Stoppard

The first comprehensive, fully illustrated guide to healthy living for people aged fifty and beyond, by top medical writer and media personality, Dr Miriam Stoppard.

A Good Start   Louise Graham

Factual and practical, full of tips on providing a healthy and balanced diet for young children, *A Good Start* is essential reading for all parents.

How to Get Off Drugs   Ira Mothner and Alan Weitz

This book is a vital contribution towards combating drug addiction in Britain in the eighties. For drug abusers, their families and their friends.

Naturebirth   Danaë Brook

A pioneering work which includes suggestions on diet and health, exercises and many tips on the 'natural' way to prepare for giving birth in a joyful relaxed way.

Pregnancy   Dr Jonathan Scher and Carol Dix

Containing the most up-to-date information on pregnancy – the effects of stress, sexual intercourse, drugs, diet, late maternity and genetic disorders – this book is an invaluable and reassuring guide for prospective parents.

Care of the Dying   Richard Lamerton

It is never true that 'nothing more can be done' for the dying. This book shows us how to face death without pain, with humanity, with dignity and in peace.

PENGUIN HEALTH

Audrey Eyton's F-Plus Audrey Eyton

'Your short cut to the most sensational diet of the century' – *Daily Express*

Baby and Child Penelope Leach

A beautifully illustrated and comprehensive handbook on the first five years of life. 'It stands head and shoulders above anything else available at the moment' – Mary Kenny in the *Spectator*

Woman's Experience of Sex Sheila Kitzinger

Fully illustrated with photographs and line drawings, this book explores the riches of women's sexuality at every stage of life. 'A book which any mother could confidently pass on to her daughter – and her partner too' – *Sunday Times*

Food Additives Erik Millstone

Eat, drink and be worried? Erik Millstone's hard-hitting book contains powerful evidence about the massive risks being taken with the health of the consumer. It takes the lid off the food we have and the food industry.

Living with Allergies Dr John McKenzie

At least 20% of the population suffer from an allergic disorder at some point in their lives and this invaluable book provides accurate and up-to-date information about the condition, where to go for help, diagnosis and cure – and what we can do to help ourselves.

Living with Stress Cary L. Cooper, Rachel D. Cooper and Lynn H. Eaker

Stress leads to more stress, and the authors of this helpful book show why low levels of stress are desirable and how best we can achieve them in today's world. Looking at those most vulnerable, they demonstrate ways of breaking the vicious circle that can ruin lives.

PENGUIN HEALTH

Medicines: A Guide for Everybody Peter Parish

This sixth edition of a comprehensive survey of all the medicines available over the counter or on prescription offers clear guidance for the ordinary reader as well as invaluable information for those involved in health care.

Pregnancy and Childbirth Sheila Kitzinger

A complete and up-to-date guide to physical and emotional preparation for pregnancy – a must for all prospective parents.

The Penguin Encyclopaedia of Nutrition John Yudkin

This book cuts through all the myths about food and diets to present the real facts clearly and simply. 'Everyone should buy one' – *Nutrition News and Notes*

The Parents' A to Z Penelope Leach

For anyone with a child of 6 months, 6 years or 16 years, this guide to all the little problems involved in their health, growth and happiness will prove reassuring and helpful.

Jane Fonda's Workout Book

Help yourself to better looks, superb fitness and a whole new approach to health and beauty with this world-famous and fully illustrated programme of diet and exercise advice.

Alternative Medicine Andrew Stanway

Dr Stanway provides an objective and practical guide to thirty-two alternative forms of therapy – from Acupuncture and the Alexander Technique to Macrobiotics and Yoga.

FOR THE BEST IN PAPERBACKS, LOOK FOR THE 🐧

PENGUIN HEALTH

Acupuncture for Everyone   Dr Ruth Lever

An examination of one of the world's oldest known therapies used by the Chinese for over two thousand years.

Aromatherapy for Everyone   Robert Tisserand

The use of aromatic oils in massage can relieve many ailments and alleviate stress and related symptoms.

Chiropractic for Everyone   Anthea Courtenay

Back pain is both extremely common and notoriously difficult to treat. Chiropractic offers a holistic solution to many of the causes through manipulation of the spine.

Herbal Medicine for Everyone   Michael McIntyre

An account of the way in which the modern herbalist works and a discussion of the wide-ranging uses of herbal medicine.

Homoeopathy for Everyone   Drs Sheila and Robin Gibson

The authors discuss the ways in which this system of administering drugs – by exciting similar symptoms in the patient – can help a range of disorders from allergies to rheumatism.

Hypnotherapy for Everyone   Dr Ruth Lever

This book demonstrates that hypnotherapy is a real alternative to conventional healing methods in many ailments.

Osteopathy for Everyone   Paul Masters

By helping to restore structural integrity and function, the osteopath gives the whole body an opportunity to achieve health and harmony and eliminate ailments from migraines to stomach troubles.

Spiritual and Lay Healing   Philippa Pullar

An invaluable new survey of the history of healing that sets out to separate the myths from the realities.